'What's wron[g] [with] ambitions?

'You do,' Kendal continued.

'That's different,' Jarrad responded.

'Why? Because I was a wife and mother?'

'As far as I'm concerned, you still are!' His temper was clearly near boiling.

'And I suppose that means I should be in your kitchen! In your bed!'

'And what's wrong with that? At least *half* the time, anyway!'

It was all she could do not to fling at him that she *had* been there—always. She'd been his for the taking, too crazily in love with him, even without the devastating ecstasies he had branded upon her body.

Always his, until Lauren had intruded...

Elizabeth Power was born in Bristol where she lives with her husband in a three-hundred-year-old cottage. A keen reader, as a teenager she had already made up her mind to be a novelist, although it wasn't until around thirty that she took up writing seriously. As an animal lover, with a strong leaning towards vegetarianism, her interests include organic vegetable gardening, regular exercise, listening to music, fashion and ministering to the demands of her adopted, generously proportioned cat!

Recent titles by the same author:

MARRYING THE ENEMY!

THE
DISOBEDIENT WIFE

BY
ELIZABETH POWER

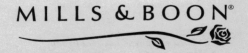

MILLS & BOON®

MILLS & BOON and MILLS & BOON with the Rose Device are registered trademarks of the publisher.

*First published in Great Britain 1997
Harlequin Mills & Boon Limited,
Eton House, 18-24 Paradise Road, Richmond, Surrey TW9 1SR*

© Elizabeth Power 1997

ISBN 0 263 80486 0

*Set in Times Roman 10 on 11 pt.
01-9712-57466 C1*

*Printed and bound in Great Britain
by Mackays of Chatham PLC, Chatham*

CHAPTER ONE

'Now let's get this straight!'

Jarrad swung away from the window, the angry glitter in his cold blue eyes displacing the shock in the autocratic framework of his hard, handsome face, a face she had fallen so desperately in love with nearly three years ago. Only this wasn't three years ago—it was now, Kendal reminded herself bitterly, the head she flung up revealing features that were both delicate and vulnerable—the red of her controlled, wild hair evincing an equally controlled yet fiery nature as she faced the man standing, glowering at her from behind the desk, bracing herself for the onslaught she had expected would follow.

'You walk out of my life nearly a year ago. Disappear for six months so that I don't know where the hell you are or what you're doing, and then you calmly waltz in here and inform me that you're going abroad—*and* taking my child with you! Well, I'm sorry, Kendal, but the answer's no. A definite and categorical no!'

Tension gripped her insides as he turned again to glare out on the sunny June morning and the city traffic seven floors below.

London was going about its business, a silent world behind the effective double glazing, effective and efficient like the man who stood with his back turned squarely against her, every muscle taut with opposition from those wide shoulders down to that lean, hard waist beneath the fine tailoring of his shirt. The man who owned not just Third Millennium Systems International—one of *the* names in computer software—but the very building it stood in. And who, until a year ago, had thought he owned her,

Kendal Mitchell... She tasted his name like some bitter elixir she had had no will to resist taking. Her, as well as their little son, Matthew.

'You seem to forget something, Jarrad.' Her voice was steady, concealing the nerves that racked her at just having to face him again. 'Believe it or not, he's *our* son.'

Those dark features, always somewhat uncompromising, were close to formidable as he turned back to her, that high forehead and straight, aristocratic nose harshened by the steely determination of that forceful jaw and that almost black hair that grew, thick and springy, to curl just below his immaculate white collar.

'I'm glad you reminded me.' That voice, deep and richly toned—that once had rendered her helpless with its powers of seduction—was now strung only with sarcasm. 'I was of the opinion that you thought I had no right to even see Matthew—let alone have any say in his future. What have you been doing anyway for the past six months?' He came round and positioned himself on the edge of the desk, just in front of her, exuding a raw energy from the disciplined fitness in the long, hard lines of his body. 'Where the hell have you been?'

Hardly daring to breathe, in case the slightest movement should cause her to accidentally touch him, Kendal refused to shrink back against her seat as every instinct was warning her she should.

'I needed the break. I had to get away.' Darn it! Why are you letting him make you sound so defensive? she berated herself, hearing her own voice croak. 'I went to Scotland.'

'Working?'

'No.'

One of those thick eyebrows lifted in almost mocking scepticism. 'So the world of interior design has had to manage without you for a while?'

She didn't respond. She knew only too well what he

thought about her working. Wasn't that what most of the rows had been about?

'So why Scotland?'

Beneath the chic green suit she could feel herself growing clammy under his harsh interrogation, but with feigned nonchalance she lifted one elegantly padded shoulder. 'Why *not* Scotland?'

'Answer me!'

Kendal's breath seemed to lock in her lungs. What could she say? *Because when you knew where I was you wouldn't leave me alone! Because you knew that if you kept on at me enough I'd come back, that I wouldn't be able to resist you!* It was the one reason she had jumped at the chance of this job in the States—to get away from him. From the fear of ever again succumbing to his lethal sexuality.

That impervious note in his voice compelled her to respond. 'It was the farthest place I could think of from London where I could be on my own for a while. Where I could think.'

'So now you've thought and you've decided you want to use your impeccable talents where the opportunities are and carve out a name for yourself in the New World—with Matthew in tow. Is that it, dearest?' There was nothing but sheer, undiluted menace behind his smile.

'No, I—' He was making it sound so mercenary. As though money was the only thing that mattered.

'Oh, don't be modest, darling. If I recall, you used to have clients clamouring by the dozen. I seem to remember you being on the phone from morning till night!'

'Hardly,' she uttered in defence of herself, of the small business she had needed, and had been trying to build through the long, last traumatic weeks of her marriage. 'And it isn't only for money,' she felt the need to tell him. 'If I'd wanted money I could have come to you.'

'Yes.' His chest expanded beneath the pristine white shirt, and for a moment she almost imagined his sigh to be one of audible regret because, of course, he knew that that was the last thing in the world she would ever have done. 'But it's something else, isn't it, Kendal? It's the buzz you get out of that stubborn need to be independent—the climb to the top regardless.'

'It isn't regardless!' A toss of her bright head revealed the long, slender line of her throat, the pulse beating angrily in its secret hollow. 'And what's wrong with my having ambitions anyway?' Again she could feel the age-old arguments surfacing, refusing to be quelled. 'You do.'

'That's different.'

'Why? Because I was a wife and mother?'

'As far as I'm concerned you still are!' His tone was angry, his temper near boiling.

'And I suppose that means I should be in your kitchen? In your bed?'

'And what's wrong with that? At least *half* the time anyway!'

'Ha ha!' It was all she could do not to fling at him that she *had* been there—always. Had been his for the taking, her heart, mind and soul too crazily in love with him even without the devastating ecstasies he had branded upon her body. Always his, until Lauren had intruded...

For a moment she felt his eyes, like twin lasers, burning through the thin veneer of her composure. A tendril of hair had come loose from her carefully arranged French pleat, and she fastened the recalcitrant red strand behind her ear with surprisingly shaky fingers, sensing those shrewd eyes following her every movement, those proud nostrils distend as though seeking the familiar scent of her perfume.

The briefest smile caused his mouth to curve with devastating sensuality, and Kendal's nerves seemed to stretch taut as she recalled how often that look had preceded nights of endless ecstasy in his arms.

'You turn up here, looking like some model off a cat-walk, in the colour I always told you suited you best, reeking to high heaven of Givenchy. What was all this intended to do, darling?' The smile was gone now. 'Soften me up?

Remind me of what I've been missing all these months and get me to agree to your ludicrous, and, if I might say so, characteristically selfish request?'

So he wouldn't allow Matthew to go.

Kendal's spirits sank although her head came up in a bright flame of defiance as she breathed through glossed lips. 'Did anybody ever have the power to soften you, Jarrad?'

He sank his hands into his pockets, which brought her gaze reluctantly to his hard abdomen and the taut fitness of his thighs beneath the expensive cut of dark suit trousers.

'You should know,' he rasped, and for a moment something murky and tumultuous clouded the usual vital glitter in his eyes. 'Although "soft" is probably far from how I would describe my responses to you.'

Kendal's heart struck up a crazy rhythm, and colour showed on the pale sheen of her cheeks.

'You would say something like that, wouldn't you?' she accused him breathlessly, jumping up to put a safer distance between herself and that potent, powerful masculinity.

'Why not?' His mockery was harsh, relentless. 'It was about the only thing that was any good between us.'

'No, you're wrong!' She wanted to forget it, to deny, if only to herself, that she had ever derived pleasure from this man's lovemaking, that he had taken her, sobbing, mindless, through the very gates of paradise. 'There was only Matthew!'

'Ah yes, Matthew…'   He straightened and moved away from the desk, his height topping hers by half a head. The lean athleticism of his body and that compelling presence that had never failed to take her breath away succeeded now, so that for a moment her defences were stripped and impetuously she blurted out, 'You've got to let me go.'

'Why?'

There was danger in his cool study, and a flash of panic showed beneath the unusual green of her eyes.

'I'm not stopping you,' he said, turning away.

'You know what I mean.' She could hear herself starting to beg. 'I mean Matthew. You've got to let me take him—'

'No!' The sheer violence of his refusal made her visibly flinch as he swung back to face her. 'I haven't *got* to do anything,' he reminded her with cruel, intimidating softness.

'So I lose the chance of this contract? Just because you're being so petty-minded?'

She watched him go back to his desk and sit down, as though he were merely discussing a matter of the day's filing.

'I don't call it being petty-minded—wanting to keep my son where I can be directly involved with his upbringing.' He took the top off his pen, the gold fountain pen he always used, the one that she had given him for his thirty-second birthday two years ago. 'You can go without him.'

Kendal caught her breath. 'You know I won't do that,' she said, moving back over to the desk.

'I know.'

Unbelievably he had resumed writing, that dark head bent in concentration. Scribbling some trifling note to his secretary, probably! she thought, frustration overcoming her so that before she could control herself she was grabbing the note from under that long, tanned hand.

'You bastard!' The crumpled paper hit his cheek before dropping onto the thick carpet beside his chair.

'Yes!' She gasped as with lightning reflexes he caught her wrist, twisting her arm, forcing her over the desk towards him. 'But then we already know that, don't we? Which is probably the reason you married me!'

She laughed in spite of the turbulent sensations that were gushing through her from the contact of those hard, tenacious fingers, a contact that was designed merely to humiliate—to crush.

'Oh, sure! Spitefulness and brutality appeals to me!' she

breathed, her green eyes dancing. 'Aren't you getting confused with the reason I left?'

She tried to wrest her hand from his, the struggle only succeeding in loosening the clasp in her hair, bringing a sea of red waves tumbling down across her shoulder.

'Now, that's how I like you.' He grunted in cold approval. 'Ruffled and undignified and stripped of all those falsely cultivated airs! And perhaps you'd mind telling me again just why you walked out on me, Kendal? And don't try to convince yourself I was anything other than tender with you. Except, of course, when you wanted me to be otherwise…'

It took all her strength, but she managed to free herself as everything that was feminine in her throbbed with the recollection of just how tender this man knew how to be.

'Wasn't incarceration and infidelity enough? You wanted a dutiful little wife at home while you carried on your secret little liaison with Lauren Westgate! Only it wasn't secret, was it, Jarrad? Ralph found out—which was the real reason he had to go! Why you fired him! You and Lauren!'

The big swivel chair squeaked beneath Jarrad's weight as he leaned back, draping one white-sleeved arm over the padded leather.

'My relationship with Lauren had nothing to do with why your brother-in-law had to leave the company,' he said with a grim cast to his mouth.

'Like hell!' she spat back, her eyes dark and wounded. It had been like twisting a knife in an already open wound when he had had her sister's accountant husband struck off his payroll. Quiet, gentle Ralph, who had reluctantly given in to her demands to tell her what he knew, had confirmed what she had already suspected was happening between Jarrad and his lovely sales director. That raw wound had split wide open, producing scars that had never healed, when she had been left to witness the turmoil into which Jarrad's action had plunged her own's sister's marriage, causing Chrissie to lose the baby she had been expecting.

Then there had been the financial problems. Ralph's loss of self-esteem. The final break-up...

'You wanted brains and breeding and you got it, didn't you? Brains in the office and a dumb, unsuspecting redhead to breed with at home!'

'And Kendal Mitchell's made up her mind about that, and nothing I say could ever convince her otherwise, could it?' Jarrad said roughly.

Try me! Give me some proof that there was never anything between you and Lauren! Foolishly, even now, her heart cried out to him, although he hadn't tried to offer any proof of it then. Nor had he done so when he had hounded her for those first six months after she'd left, demanding that she return home, and only for his son's sake, though he hadn't said that in so many words. But of course she knew it was only because of Matthew.

'You're right! Nothing can—or ever will!' she flung at him, and turned on her heel, wanting to get out of there before the tears of frustration and regret she could feel burning behind her eyes threatened to degrade her in front of him.

'Kendal!'

She froze on the spot, his imperious tone forcing her to glance back over her shoulder.

'I meant what I said. You take that job in the States and you go on your own.'

'And if I don't?' she challenged.

'Then I'll sue for custody.'

Kendal's teeth sank into the inner flesh of her bottom lip. 'You wouldn't be that callous,' she whispered.

'Try me.'

'You'd never get it!'

'Why not?' That hard, cruel mouth pulled down on one side. 'An incarcerating and unfaithful husband,' he said, using her own description of him, 'doesn't necessarily make for a poor father in English law.'

He was right, of course, and he would use every shred

of power and influence he possessed to see it turned out his way. She knew from experience that Jarrad Mitchell always got what he wanted.

'Get lost!' she breathed, turning away, battling against an inner surge of panic.

'No, that's been your prerogative, darling.' She heard his voice coming mockingly from behind her. 'But not any more. Aren't you rather forgetting something?'

She stopped in her tracks and turned back to him, frowning.

'The address of where you're staying,' he supplied emotionlessly. And then, when she hesitated, he said, 'Unless, of course, you'd prefer to give it to my solicitor.'

He meant it! Oh, dear heaven.

As he got to his feet she wanted to claw his arrogant face with her carefully lacquered nails, because, of course, he'd been right when he'd said she had hoped that seeing her would soften him into submission. But Jarrad Mitchell never submitted to anyone, she remembered bitingly. He only ever controlled.

Well, get this! she thought, leaning on her small green handbag and scrawling the address of her new flat in the notebook she always carried, which contained the names of useful contacts in the design world. I'm going to take up your challenge of a fight and just for once I'm going to win!

Nevertheless her spirit masked a very strong element of doubt and not a little fear as she tore the page out of her notebook and flung it in the direction of her husband's daunting figure, unaware of his cool amusement as the page fluttered under his desk from the sudden draught caused as she swept out of his office.

'So what did he say?'

There was eager anticipation in Chrissie Langdon's question as she watched her sister sip the sweet, hot tea she had made her.

'You wouldn't believe it!'

Five years older than Chrissie, Kendal wasn't usually one to pour out her troubles to her sister, especially since, during the past year or so, Chrissie had had enough problems of her own. Today, though, it was obvious to Chrissie that her sister was clearly in a state.

'Oh, I would! Believe me, where Jarrad Mitchell's concerned, I would!' Chrissie breathed, rolling large brown eyes emphasised by her small face and her short, spiky brown hair. She darted a glance to eighteen-month-old Matthew, whom she had been looking after that morning, and who had just discovered that hurling a book across the carpet was far more exciting than turning its pages. 'Go on. Fire away.'

Kendal put down her cup and saucer on the wicker table which formed part of the rustic, bohemian furnishings that Chrissie loved. In fact, when Chrissie had moved into the Victorian semi with Ralph three years ago—newly married and spending money like water—Kendal recalled how she had tried to help her economise, suggesting cost-cutting ways with the design.

Now, though, being in the same position as Kendal was, and between jobs as an office receptionist, Kendal knew that if it hadn't been for the proceeds of their old home—half of which she had released to Chrissie on her last birthday, the other half of which she had put in trust for Matthew—her sister would have had difficulty keeping up payments on the house even when she was in full-time employment.

Now she sat back, took a deep breath and said, 'He's going to sue for custody.'

Chrissie whistled under her breath. 'What? If you go abroad? Or in any case?' she appended, suddenly looking aghast, and Kendal groaned. She hadn't actually considered that he might do it regardless.

'I think he meant if I take this job.'

'So what will you do?' Chrissie sank down onto the low floral-patterned sofa opposite her older sister. 'Not bother?'

Kendal gave her an exasperated look. 'Chrissie! That would just be giving in to him. I'll go—and with Matthew—and I'll fight Jarrad every step of the way!'

'You might live to regret that.' Chrissie picked up the cup of herbal tea she had made for herself. 'The man's a fighter, Kendal. And the worst possible kind. He doesn't take any prisoners. He'll chew you up and spit you out and have you crawling back to him for mercy before it ever comes to court. Jarrad Mitchell can do *anything*!'

Kendal grimaced, and yet was unable to contain a fleeting smile as she glanced sideways and saw Matthew, sitting surrounded by the scattered pages of his little picture book, beaming up at her in wide-eyed innocence. 'You make him sound like some sort of mythical demon,' she uttered with an inexplicable little shudder as she reached for her cup and saucer. 'And as though you almost admire him for it!' she went on to chide disbelievingly, although she knew that wasn't far from the truth.

From the moment Chrissie had met Jarrad at her own wedding three years ago she had looked up to him with the kind of hero-worship one would expect from a naive teenager—which of course she had been then—and, surprisingly she still displayed it to some degree, despite the brutal way in which he had treated her husband.

'It's his determination I admire—that scary determination that ensures nobody and nothing gets in his way and makes everybody respect him,' Chrissie stated almost contentiously. 'I wish Ralph had had just a quarter of it. Perhaps if he had, we'd still be…' She shrugged as though she'd learnt from the pains of over a year without the good-looking, quiet-voiced accountant that it was no use wishing.

'And he's not a demon—just a man,' she went on in that same, near-contentious tone, although it took Kendal a second or two to realise that she was still referring to Jarrad. 'But as I said he's a very determined one. Determined, tough and a lot more capable of withstanding the sort of emotional pressure that a battle like this is going to put on you. You can't take him on, Kendal. For heaven's sake, compromise! Meet him halfway or something.'

Kendal looked at her sister obliquely. 'You mean give up the chance of this job?'

For a moment something glittered in those dark eyes, and Kendal was struck by Chrissie's likeness to her father. But then she had inherited his dark hair and complexion too, Kendal thought, remembering the father who had abandoned them without a care. He had left his wife and children for another woman, only to desert again after Jane Harringdale had taken him back—an act, Kendal reflected painfully now, that had proved too much for their mother's poor health and had ultimately brought on that fatal collapse.

'Apart from a few months while you were having Matthew, you've always been working.' It was a reproof, and yet it sounded like a complaint, too, from Chrissie.

'I've had to,' Kendal stressed quietly. When their mother had died eight years ago Chrissie had been just thirteen, and Kendal herself only eighteen, and Robert Harringdale hadn't wanted to know. It had been a struggle, therefore, bringing up her sister alone, doing office work during the day while studying for her qualifications as an interior designer at night—particularly as Chrissie hadn't been an easy teenager, always critical of herself as well as others, often questioning her own worth. As one so-called expert had remarked at the time, she had blamed both her parents for leaving her.

Consequently, desperate for love, and despite Kendal's attempts to be both mother and father to her, Chrissie had married the first man who had come along shortly before her eighteenth birthday. And, with Ralph being ten years older and therefore more mature, it might have worked out, Kendal thought—eventually. If it hadn't been for that cold, calculated act of Jarrad's...

'So what if you win?' Chrissie was leaning back against the cushions, playing with an overhanging leaf from one of the plants that grew in abundance around the room. 'You'll just be a single mum in a strange country. And, looking at it from a rather selfish point of view, when will I ever get to see you?'

Kendal gave her a dry smile. 'You can come with me,' she invited gently—tentatively—but Chrissie merely grimaced.

'Thanks, but no thanks,' she stated in a rather flat tone, and, sadly, Kendal realised that all her sister wanted—hoped for—was a reconciliation with Ralph.

'You'll be working flat out. You'll have to—to keep yourself and Matthew, 'cos I know you'll never accept a penny from Jarrad. You've said so often enough,' Chrissie expressed. 'Though I can't think why! He's rich enough to keep you, Matthew and half of London besides!'

And clever enough to know that if I take anything from him I'll be surrendering my independence to him, Kendal thought, which is what he wants. But she didn't say it.

'I don't mind working. I need it,' she tagged on, unable to add, I need it to help me forget him. To stop driving myself mad with thinking about him. And if I'm abroad he can't find me so easily. Can't hurt me any more.

'It's not just Matthew. He wants you as well. You know that, don't you?' Chrissie interrupted her thoughts as if she had read them. 'Oh, Kendal, you could have so much if you'd only swallow your pride and give him another chance.'

Her cup suspended in mid-air, Kendal stared at her sister aghast. 'Go back to him, you mean? Take him back? Like Mum did with Dad!'

'Oh, for heaven's sake! Jarrad's nothing like him!' the younger girl stated adamantly. 'You could do worse, you know. And it would be a proper family life for Matthew. I don't suppose you can blame him for wanting that.'

Kendal looked down at her son, who was chewing the

cover of his book and gurgling contentedly to himself. Wasn't that what she wanted for her child? A stable home? She wanted it more than anything. Did her sister imagine that it had been easy these past twelve months? Because it hadn't been. It had been hell…

'And what about me? What are you suggesting, Chrissie? That I shouldn't have left him? That I should have been content to be his housemaid and his dutiful little sex slave while he carried on with that patronising Lauren Westgate behind my back?'

'Of course I'm not suggesting you should be that,' Chrissie was quick to respond. 'Although I don't think you should pretend you didn't enjoy the role, or that part of it at any rate—sleeping with him, I mean—because you were besotted with him. Everyone could see it. You worshipped the ground he walked on!'

A flame, which Kendal had thought successfully banked down until she'd faced Jarrad in his office today now leapt to sudden, vibrant life again, way down in her loins.

'More fool me!'

'And you were hardly his housemaid.'

No. There had been the long-standing Teeny Roberts to cook and clean. He hadn't intended her to do all that—even if she had had the time. And perhaps that might have been the problem, in part…

'As for Lauren, she did rather throw herself at him,' Chrissie reminded her. 'And a man with his looks is going to get that every day of the week! It would take a monk to resist that constant barrage from the opposite sex. And I'm not prepared to believe he was even having an affair with her. He's never actually admitted it, has he?'

No, he hadn't, Kendal thought. But she had found those receipts in his study from the hotel where they had stayed when he had told her simply that he was away working, had led her to believe he'd gone alone. Oh, they'd been under separate names—and in separate rooms—it was true. But then anything else wouldn't have looked too good if those receipts had wound up in his accounts office for Ralph to find! Only they hadn't needed to. Being caught together in Jarrad's office, as they had been by her brother-in-law that night, was all the evidence that mattered!

'He's never actually denied it either.' How could he? When such a denial would have been a blatant lie! 'I don't know how you can defend him, Chrissie! After what he did to Ralph!'

Chrissie lowered her gaze, looking so unhappy suddenly that Kendal wished she hadn't said anything.

'I'm sorry,' was all she could utter, wishing she could wave a magic wand and make everything all right, for her sister at least.

'Oh, that's all right. I'm getting used to it now,' Chrissie expressed resignedly, although Kendal knew she was just putting on a brave face. 'Perhaps he did fire Ralph because he thought he was checking up on him. I don't know,' she went on to remark disconsolately. 'But I think a lot of the blame for what happened has to rest with Ralph himself.'

She glanced away, picking distractedly at the edging of one of the plump multi-floral scatter cushions, looking decidedly uneasy. 'I think it got to the stage where he couldn't—couldn't cope with—things…'

'What sort of things?' Kendal enquired, frowning. She knew her sister wasn't the easiest of people to live with.

'Oh…just things in general,' Chrissie remarked evasively, continuing to pick at the blanket-stitched cushion with unusual agitation. But then Matthew ran up to her, waving one of his little striped socks, and laughingly she hauled him up onto her lap.

'Anyway, what I'm saying is I don't think you should blame him entirely for Ralph losing his job—even if you'd like to.' She was bent in concentration over the gurgling Matthew, diligently pulling the sock over a tiny foot. 'And what if he did have one fling? It isn't the end of the world. And perhaps he did feel neglected. After all, the more he told you he didn't like you working, the more contracts you

seemed determined to take on just to show him—out of
sheer defiance.'

Kendal bit her lip. Did Chrissie really think that?

'I did it for my own sanity,' was all she could say.
Because the truth was that if she hadn't resumed her pro-
fession after Matthew had been born—plunged herself
wholeheartedly into her work—she would have gone mad,
crazy with doubt and suspicion.

It had been bad enough that she hadn't felt needed in the
home, without Lauren constantly flaunting her success and
her very enviable working relationship with Jarrad whenever Kendal, with silent reluctance, had had to preside over
dinner parties that included the other woman. It had only
just been bearable at first, when she had had her own job,
her own career. But those years of domesticity and studying
when she had been looking after her sister hadn't prepared
her for the condescending confidence of women like Lauren
Westgate.

Consequently, when she'd surrendered her self-
sufficiency to have Matthew, and had been insecure as a
new mother, Lauren's belittling remarks about women who
were 'stuck at home', and Kendal being 'just a housewife'—coupled with Jarrad suddenly spending more and
more time away from home—had all helped drive her back
into the safe, secure world of her beloved decor and design.
She had wanted to prove herself, and not only to herself
but to her husband and the world that she could be just as
shining and successful in her own way as Lauren Westgate
could. And not only that, but that she could be a success—
needed—as a wife and mother as well. And all she had got
for her trouble—her foolish, impetuous naivety—was the
proverbial slap in the face when her efforts only succeeded
in driving her husband right into the other woman's arms!

'Anyway,' she attempted to say lightly. 'I suppose it's
only natural you should defend him, knowing what you
think of women with children working!'

Chrissie clung fervently to the belief that being a housewife and mother was a full-time job, and Kendal knew her sister had settled down enough to take on both roles with avid dedication, which made that last miscarriage and subsequent break-up of her own marriage such a tragedy.

With one shriek their attention was drawn to Matthew who, having pulled off the sock which had been painstakingly restored to his foot, now held it up triumphantly. He squealed a protest as Chrissie tried to clasp him to her, grizzling until she released him, so that he could run on unsteady little legs across the carpet, arms outstretched, to his mother.

'You're a scamp!' Kendal breathed, hauling him up onto her lap. 'First Chrissie. Now me. You don't know who you want, do you?'

'Kissie,' he gurgled in his baby mimicry, then rewarded Kendal with a chop to the nose with his little flying fist, still tightly clenched around the sock.

Both girls laughed.

'I don't know where you get your energy from,' Chrissie told him as he strained round to look at her, and stuck a determined little foot into Kendal's groin in the process.

'Oh, I do,' Kendal exhaled, wincing, putting a hand under his bottom to transfer him gently to a less sensitive area of her body. He shrieked a protest at even that small amount of restraint. 'Believe me, I certainly do!'

Because, whether she wanted to admit it to anyone else or not, she couldn't help but admit to herself that he was very much Jarrad's child. From that crop of brown hair—growing darker by the day—to the very feet of the long little body that determined that one day he would be tall, like his father, to that burgeoning self-sufficiency that was apparent even in his babyhood. She almost imagined she could already feel that restless determination and energy in him that was so characteristic of Jarrad Mitchell—so characteristic it scared her that she might never be free of the man's memory.

The only part of her it seemed her son had inherited was

those green-flecked, big, beguiling eyes—eyes that Jarrad had once jokingly announced could 'smite a man at twenty paces'. And with that combination of physical assets and character Kendal could see that Matthew was already destined to break a few hearts.

'Just like his dad,' Chrissie supplied—reading her thoughts again, Kendal thought, startled, until she realised her sister was still referring to something they had been saying a moment ago.

'No, not like his dad,' she couldn't help responding nevertheless, on the smallest note of panic, and she clutched her son tightly to her—ignoring his flailing fists now, his straining efforts to free himself—as though she would protect him from the world and anything that threatened to taint him with the same ability to hurt and wound as Jarrad Mitchell had hurt and wounded her. As, similarly, her own father had hurt and destroyed her mother.

'I've got to take that job, Chrissie,' she breathed over her son's angry, lemon-clad little shoulder. *I've got to get away from him.* And more determinedly, aloud again, she uttered, 'I've got to go.'

CHAPTER TWO

AFTER dropping Matthew off with her child minder later that afternoon, Kendal drove out to see some clients for whom she had agreed to do some freelance work, her first since coming back to London. The woman and her husband had approached her through her old firm, having been pleased with the work she had done for them in the past.

She hated leaving her son, particularly twice in one day, because every time she watched him toddle away from her it was like losing a part of herself. But she knew what the alternative would mean—being beholden to Jarrad. Oh, she didn't mind that for Matthew's sake, because she knew her husband wouldn't stop short of providing more than a generous allowance for his son.

But she needed to keep herself too. The savings she had accumulated before leaving the matrimonial home a year ago were now nearly exhausted, and there was no way that she intended to take any money from a man who not only flaunted his mistress openly in her face but who could be so callous as to do what he had done to Ralph—because it had been callous, no matter what Chrissie said.

Forcing herself to forget Jarrad, she focused her thoughts on the job ahead. She had her sketchbook, notepad, colour charts...

She made a quick note in her mind of everything she would need, after negotiating one particularly busy junction, and by the time she pulled onto the drive of the large mock-Georgian house she was mentally as well as physically prepared.

Jill and Peter Arkwright were a middle-aged couple, with two golden Retrievers who sat obediently looking at Kendal from a hopeful distance as she nibbled the oversized slice of rich sponge cake that Jill had insisted Kendal have with her coffee. At the same time, diligently she sketched her plan for the ornamental mouldings and alcoves she had suggested for the lounge, to help take the squareness off the large room.

By the time she left she had a very clear picture of what they needed. An overall classic but country feel that would give the prestigious yet modern estate house some individuality.

Keen to get started, so that the job would be completed if Jarrad did back down and let her take Matthew away—which she very much doubted—she drove straight back home, deciding to pick the little boy up within the hour. In the meantime she had colours to decide on, fabrics to order, painting contractors and carpenters to organise.

Home was a furnished ground-floor flat in an Edwardian terraced house which she was renting on a month-to-month basis until she knew what her definite plans were, therefore the furnishings weren't at all what she would have chosen herself. It was, however, situated in a quiet street, in a reasonably quiet suburb of the city.

As it was a pleasingly warm day she had the French windows open while she worked, and was enjoying the lucid song of a blackbird above the more distant sounds of afternoon traffic, above the sudden low drone of a car pulling up somewhere along the road.

She answered the phone breezily when it rang. 'Kendal Mitchell.'

'How did you get on with the Arkwrights?'

The pleasant male voice brought an instant smile to her lips.

'Tony! Hi!'

'Was she still as generous with the cake rations?'

Kendal laughed. 'You'd better believe it!' She liked Tony Beeson. They were roughly the same age and had worked together at the same design firm until Kendal had married. In fact Tony still worked for them, and it was he who had told her about the job that was going in the States, after visiting his brother's family in Philadelphia.

'Made up your mind yet whether you're going to be leaving us?' He sounded tentative. In a way he had opened this opportunity for her, but, now that it looked as if it might materialise, Kendal knew he didn't really want her to go.

'Not yet,' she parried, not wanting to go into detail. Tony knew she was separated, but that was all. She didn't see any point in discussing the obstructions that Jarrad might throw in her way.

'Have you ever thought about a partnership?' Tony surprised her by suddenly asking.

Kendal frowned, hesitated. 'A partnership?'

'Yes, dumbo. A partnership. You and me. Just say the word and I'd come with you. We'd make a very good team, you know, with your creative flair and my cock-eyed business sense. What do you say? Just the two of us?'

Kendal laughed awkwardly. She had never actually dated Tony and wasn't sure whether he was serious or not.

'You mean you running the business side and me showing all those Yankees what an English home really should look like?'

'Why not?' he suggested, sounding even more serious. 'No strings attached. Unless, of course, you wanted there to be.'

She laughed again because she didn't know what else to do.

'I can't wait to see that!' she jested, ignoring that last bit about strings. But, no, she decided. Partnerships, of any kind, were out. Two healthy, attractive people of opposite genders couldn't work closely together without sex getting in the way. Jarrad and Lauren were evidence of that. Besides, she had been wary of men before marrying Jarrad—and with good reason—and she intended being nothing but wary ever again.

'Come with me by all means, but let's just stick to the

wildly passionate affair we've got now, shall we?' she continued to jest, hoping she was letting him down lightly. 'A working relationship will only taint it. I've seen it happen so many times.'

She heard Tony's deep, expressive sigh. 'Alas, so have I.' She could almost picture him then, with his hand on his heart. 'Well, after that very positive rebuff I'd better go, angel.' So he was only half joking. 'I'll call you again—if my wounded pride will let me. Love you.'

Kendal beamed into the mouthpiece. 'I love you too,' she breathed out of sheer relief as she heard his end of the line go dead.

She replaced the receiver, a soft smile touching her lips as she glanced absently towards the patio doors. And then her smile faded, every nerve seeming to freeze, as she met the hard features of the broad-shouldered man standing there, framed by the aperture.

'Jarrad!'

His shoes made no sound on the carpet as he came in, danger in every lean inch of his arrogant frame and in those determinedly slow strides.

'So that's why you're headed off halfway across the world. You've got yourself a boyfriend. Is that why you're looking so shocked, darling?' Mockery couldn't soften those austerely beautiful features. 'What were you hoping? That I wouldn't find out?'

From behind the large old table that served as a makeshift desk, Kendal stared up at him, her pale skin drained of colour. 'I—I didn't expect you.'

A muscle pulled beside that strong jaw. 'Didn't you?' he asked roughly, picking up a rubber and tossing it down on the table again. 'I would have thought it was obvious even to you that I'd want to see my son.'

Well, of course it was. And she had known he would call. That was why she had been so reluctant to let him have her address that morning. She just hadn't anticipated that it would be so soon, that was all.

'You—you can't.' The shock of seeing him made her voice falter, and something tightened her already clenched stomach muscles as she saw those dark masculine brows draw together.

'I beg your pardon?'

Kendal swallowed. He seemed so dauntingly big, even in the fair-sized, high-ceilinged room, that she struggled to her feet so as not to feel at such a disadvantage.

'I mean…he's with Valerie—my child minder. I haven't picked him up yet.' And that was the worst thing she could have said, she realised, when she saw the thunderous look that crossed his harshly sculptured face.

'Of course. Ever the dutiful mother.' Distaste twisted those grim lips as he glanced down at the emulsion charts, swatches and sketches she had been labouring over. 'I thought you said you hadn't been working.'

'I needed—' The money, she'd been about to say, but stopped herself in time. 'I found I needed to,' she corrected as calmly as she could, although she guessed he had realised why when she saw his critical appraisal of the room, with its rather world-weary-looking furniture and the plain and jaded decor.

'You bring our child from our home into a run-down place like this!' He swore rather savagely.

'It's clean and it's paid for!' Quickly Kendal hastened to defend her rather modest home. 'Anyway, it isn't going to be for very long.'

'Ah, no, I'd forgotten. And are you imagining you can allow another man into your life to take on the role of looking after *my* son?'

He had obviously overheard and misinterpreted her conversation with Tony, but she was feeling too weary to put him straight. Anyway, he had had no qualms about his own affair with Lauren.

'And what if I am?' she threw back at him, coming round the table and then suddenly wishing she had kept it between them—as a barrier against his pulsing anger—when he took a step nearer and breathed, 'Over my dead body.'

His voice was low and threatening, and she sent a glance up at him from under her lashes, somehow unable to visualise him lying prostrate and helpless. It was Jarrad Mitchell who controlled, while others fell around him in obedient submission.

'I just thought you ought to know, Jarrad.' She was level with him now, a willowy, delicate figure beside his hard, intimidating masculinity, though her face was uptilted to his in challenge. 'I'm going to fight you for him.' Her voice didn't falter. Somehow she had managed to sound miraculously calm.

Something leapt in the glacial blue of his eyes. Anger, but something else too. Something remarkably like admiration, she realised, amazed—because of course a man like him respected a healthy rival. It whetted his appetite, stimulated his competitive energies, his need to win. But all he said was, 'You stupid little fool.'

A shudder ran down her spine from remembering something Chrissie had said about crawling back to him for mercy. Nevertheless, she was determined not to let that daunting male confidence undermine her resolve.

'No, not any more, Jarrad,' she taunted softly, making to brush past him, and paid for it when he grabbed her, his clasp bruising on her upper arm as he forced her back to face him.

'Have you slept with him yet?' It was an angry, relentless demand.

'That's none of your business!' All decorum deserted her as she struggled to free herself—to no avail—from his tenacious, determined hold.

He laughed without humour. 'Well that's where you're very wrong, Kendal. It's very much my business. Particularly as it seems I have to remind you that you're still my wife!'

'I am?' She tilted her head to gaze up at him with scathing incredulity. 'That didn't seem to worry you too much when you were off having your adulterous fling with Lauren!'

'That's your interpretation of it,' he said grimly.

'And Ralph's! Were we both wrong?' Unconsciously a small, injured note had crept into her voice. 'Or are you one of these men who thinks wives should be faithful while husbands sleep with as many lovers as they think fit?'

Now mockery curled that rather cruel mouth, though his eyes were concealed by the dark sweep of his lowered lashes.

'Is that what you imagined you were, Kendal? Part of some sort of exotic harem?' His cold amusement was derisive. 'Just now there was only one!'

Only the clean, clear notes of the blackbird's song filtering in through the open doors broke the moment's silence as she glared at him, dumbfounded. 'My God! Isn't that enough?'

He caught both of her arms now, and was holding her there in front of him, the shadow that crossed his face making those dark features appear sombre, almost pained, though she knew it was only the late afternoon sun playing tricks as it fell across the lawn.

'And isn't it enough that I spent every energy I possessed in trying to make you happy? In pleasuring you, Kendal? Whatever you thought I felt for Lauren I still wanted to lose myself in you. Again and again and again. And you, you always responded to me like some crazed animal. Never able to get enough...'

She shut her mind to the images that were swimming before her eyes—the ultimate ecstasy of being dominated by the driving power of this man, the joy of being in his arms, of those pinnacles of pleasure that had had her sobbing, swept away on a tide of desire far beyond the reaches of any earthly plane. But that was before she had had positive proof that he found Lauren's company so much more stimulating, before he had sacked Ralph and she, herself, had realised the hard way that she had been wrong ever to believe anything a man said—any man...

'Things change,' was all she said, brittly, not trusting herself to utter anything else.

'Like hell!' he whispered, and then, with one hand to the base of her spine, pulled her lower body against the hard, lean angles of his.

She gasped at the startling contact, shutting her eyes tight against the sensations that ripped through her at the shocking evidence of his arousal. But a slow, insidious heat was building in her, permeating her tissues, her cells and her very blood to make her breathing quicken and her breasts strain against the white cotton of the sleeveless blouse she was wearing with the chic, straight skirt of her green suit.

'You see?' he murmured, with a soft laugh under his breath. But she couldn't see anything—not reason or logic or sense.

Beneath her resisting hands the cool fabric of his jacket sent a raw sensuality shivering through her, the dizzying fragrance of his cologne, with that more personal male scent that was as familiar to her as his signature, playing havoc with her defences. Even as some saner part of her repelled it some masochistic streak yearned for that arm that was holding her loosely to ignore any protest she might make and crush her to him, before that deeply sensual voice went on, 'We belong together, Kendal, whether you like it or not. And, if taking care and control of Matthew away from you means I keep you here, then I'll do everything in my power to effect that end.'

Oh, dear heaven...

Without realising it, she was aware now that she had walked into his trap, baited by his cruel reminder of the slave she had been to her own physical desire for him during their brief marriage.

Opening her eyes, she saw those strong features graven with wanting and desire and, above all, determination. Driven by fear—of herself more than of anything he might do—somehow she managed to utter in a voice that trembled, 'Aren't you forgetting that it isn't just you, me and Matthew any more?'

If she had been struggling for her freedom then nothing else could have been more effective in securing it, because he pushed her roughly away from him. The expression on that hard face was oddly smug, however, as though he had gained some victory in a game that could only be won round by round.

'In that case, darling, you're obviously in danger of being as unfaithful to him as I have apparently been with Lauren. And if you've got any illusions about running off with him and taking Matthew, I'd advise you now not even to entertain the idea. You're coming back to me, Kendal, sooner or later, so you'd better start getting used to the idea.

'And the next time I call I want to see my son—here—' he stabbed a hard finger towards the floor '—where he belongs, with his mother—for the time being—*if* it isn't too much trouble! Not with some hired help who's paid to step in whenever his mother decides she's too busy to care for him herself!'

His words cut her to the quick so that she almost wanted to lash out at him. But despite her quickly roused temper—even after the way he had wronged her while she had still been living with him—she had never quite degraded herself by striking him.

'How dare you?' she breathed, choking on the thought that he might even consider that she was anything but a good mother to Matthew.

'Yes, I dare,' he uttered with soft intimidation. 'It's my legal right as your husband and—more significantly—as your child's father. And talking of rights—I intend to claim them. And we'll start with visiting rights—as of now! I'll be away from tonight on a conference that's going to take at least till the middle of next week. But I'll be round again next Friday afternoon at two. Be here, and see that Matthew's here as well. I intend to take him home with me

for as long as I desire to have him. And you're coming
with him!'

'No!' Panic strung her voice at the mere thought of what
he was suggesting. Of course he could see Matthew, but
there was no way that she was going back to the matrimonial home that she had run from in such hopeless despair
a year ago.

He took no heed of her startled objection, though, only
added, 'And if you don't like it, then I'm afraid, my dearest,
you can darn well lump it, because those are the conditions.
And if he isn't here, Kendal, there'll be hell to pay!'

He stormed out then, leaving her standing, alone and
shaken, listening to the angry growl of the Porsche she
presumed he still drove. That determined thrust of power
as he pulled away reflected his mood, breaking the stillness
of the day, before he turned the corner and the growl became a roar and then faded away altogether.

After he had gone, Kendal found it impossible to concentrate, her earlier enthusiasm for the Arkwrights' job having totally deserted her.

Why couldn't he leave her alone?

The question screamed through her brain as it had done
so many times during those first six months after she had
taken Matthew and fled.

She had gone first to a hotel—because she hadn't wanted
to burden the newly separated and unhappy Chrissie—then
to the comfortable, moderately priced accommodation she
had rented to the mutual benefit of herself and an old
schoolfriend who had taken a temporary job away from
London. But Jarrad had persisted in pursuing her, which
had eventually driven her to Scotland—but of course she
knew why. There was no mystery to it. He wanted his son,
to be with him, see him grow up.

She could understand that. Didn't it hurt and distress her
enough that she had had to deprive her child of a normal
family life because of his father's infidelity, just as she and
Chrissie had been deprived because of their own father's

infidelity to their mother? But, whether she desired it or not, Jarrad also wanted her, Kendal, and she knew now that it wasn't just so that she could be a mother to Matthew.

She flopped down onto a chair, dropping her head in her hands to try and banish the shaming memory of the sensations that had flared so dangerously to life in her again the instant he had touched her, sensations she had hoped crushed by time and the torturous reality of his affair with Lauren. But they hadn't been, and she had to admit now that it wasn't just a one-sided thing—that powerful sexual chemistry that governed everything he said and did. It was totally reciprocal, and always had been, right from the first day they had met.

She had tried to ignore it at first—this mutual and terrifying attraction—to ignore the feelings that had come to startling life within her from the first moment she had seen him at Chrissie and Ralph's wedding. He had been Ralph's boss after all. But even without knowing that she wouldn't have failed to recognise those qualities that had made Jarrad Mitchell a leader—successful as well as immensely wealthy. The determined purpose, the daunting self-confidence and the compelling energy with that cool, unmistakable air of command.

These were qualities she had known and feared, had always been wary of, because hadn't her father been as successful in his own field? And just as Chrissie had fallen for and married the first man who had come into her young life, Kendal herself, conversely, had always been the cautious one. Her distrust of men had kept her aloof, with the result that she had had no more than brief, uninvolved, and certainly non-intimate relationships with the opposite sex by the time she'd met Jarrad. Nor had any other man she'd met tugged so vibrantly at her senses.

Which was why, when he'd taken her hand during their introduction after the photo session, it had been like putting a match to blue touch paper! she thought drily now.

She had managed to treat him with only polite reserve

at Chrissie's wedding, to dodge his persistent attempts, during those weeks that had followed, to get her into his life. Because he'd made that intention clear, sometimes turning up at Chrissie's, sometimes telephoning her when she'd been in the office, sometimes appearing at some social gathering where she'd happened to be, although he'd always seemed to have some practical reason for being there.

Yet, during all that time, though her physical impulses had been urging her to give in and go out with him—plunge in with both feet and embark on the most dangerous and exciting adventure of her life—her strong-willed determination—which she had often employed to control what she knew was a naturally impetuous nature, and which had kept her from getting hurt—had won. So that at last, it seemed, he had lost interest.

That was until nearly a year later, when she had been sent by her firm to use her design skills on the newly constructed, beautifully appointed home of a new client, only to find that it was him.

He had been so impeccably formal then, that she hadn't dared to question his motives. And it was just as well, she had thought with an absurd and shocked dismay at the time, as almost immediately she had discovered why she had been hired.

He was thinking of getting married, he'd told her, and wanted the best possible taste for the house he'd had specially built for his bride-to-be. He'd seen some of Kendal's artistic expertise at the home of a friend who had just happened to be one of Kendal's clients—as well as having seen it at Chrissie's—and he was giving her an entirely free hand with the decor.

She hadn't wanted to do it. She had still been daunted by the formidable strength of her dangerous fascination for him. And, as well, she'd been stupidly hurt that he could have pursued her as he had and now expected her to decorate his home for the woman he'd chosen to be his bride when she'd shown—and only for her own self-protection—

that she wasn't interested. It had been like the ultimate put-
down. Besides, she'd wondered what sort of woman he was
marrying who would welcome having her entire furnishings
chosen by someone else.

As she could give her boss no good reason for not going
ahead with the job, however, she had had little choice but
to accept it.

He had continued to treat her then only as he would have
treated any business associate. In fact during those times
when he had cause to contact her he had been almost ex-
asperatingly aloof, which, she acknowledged with bitter
irony now, had been the surest way—if he'd wanted to get
her into his bed—to make her drop her guard. And he had
known that, known how fragile her immunity to him was
by the time he'd first invited her to lunch.

When he did, however, it was purely on a business basis,
although over that first lengthy meal in that elaborate restaurant, she caught snatches of the humour that could twist
his hard mouth into a devastating smile; saw glimpses of
what she wanted to believe was the lonely man behind the
forceful dynamo she'd originally feared. The orphaned boy
come good who, despite all his riches, had no real family
of his own. The youth who had made it through a tough
secondary school and an even tougher neighbourhood to
emerge a bright scholar with eventually a university degree,
bringing all his knowledge of business systems management into a company that seemed both high-flying and secure.

When it collapsed, he was in a position to take it over,
engaging Ralph as the company accountant and the efficient
Lauren, who had been an up-and-coming manager, as his
second-in-command. And the rest, as they say, was his-
tory...

All this Kendal learned not only from snippets he
dropped in casually at that lunch but from other lunches
that followed, and from Ralph. She had been keen to pump
her brother-in-law dry, thirsty for every trickle of knowledge he could convey to her about his enigmatic employer.

She warned herself that he was marrying someone else, that the only reason he was seeing her at all was because he needed her artistic skills, that she meant nothing to him beyond a simple means to an end—and that he meant nothing to her, either. But the warnings and the false convictions fell on deaf ears. She was already desperately in love with him.

Both Chrissie and Ralph knew, of course, how crazy she was about him, although she didn't say a word to them. She worked swiftly and diligently, praying for the day when the job would be finished so that she wouldn't have to face him again—be reminded of what she had missed by snubbing him as she had originally—so that she could retreat from the folly of her hopeless emotions.

And then the lunches became the odd dinner, not in the formal hotel restaurants where he had taken her to discuss business but in cosier, more intimate little places, where they shared amusing anecdotes and exchanged confidences. And where, in spite of all that—the intimacy and the romance and the laughter—he would resort to talking about his forthcoming marriage as coldly as though none of it mattered.

And afterwards, walking her back to the car, he would resume that air of exasperating detachment until she wanted to scream with frustration, forget that he was someone else's and throw herself into those cold, indifferent arms. Sometimes she thought, with hurt and embarrassed mortification, that he knew exactly how she felt, and that he'd only engaged her after he'd decided to marry because he knew how hard he could make her fall and wanted to punish her for rejecting him as she had. The male ego being what it was, she convinced herself of it.

Only on that last day, when she called to inspect the result of the work she had put in progress, had there been any change in his attitude towards her, and then only by chance, she thought at first. She could only laugh at herself for her stupid naivety now.

They were in the master suite—of all places!—having gone through every room together so that she could satisfy herself that everything had been done according to her original plans. While he was distantly complimentary that day, praising her taste and her professional abilities, she felt as though she was dying inside, thinking that it was over, that she would never see him again.

Then she came round the bed, after checking that everything was in place in the dressing room and the *en suite* bathroom, only to trip over a corner of the duvet, and somehow—she didn't quite know how—she wound up in his arms.

He looked at her for a moment, as though seeking the mutual desire burning in her eyes that she couldn't have kept from him even if she had wanted to, her mind and body not just willing, but silently begging for the kisses he had so cleverly denied them both. Because it had been calculated, that moment of surrender, right down to the nth degree—and by a man who only played to win!

But, as she had learned through experience—and to her cost, she reflected bitterly now—one kiss between them could never be enough, just as that first kiss proved not to be. Because it hadn't been just a tender exchange of feeling between two people who might have been falling in love, but a blinding, explosive union of man and woman in a hungry meeting of mouths that had only imitated the true act, and that had had her pushing away from him in sudden realisation of the seriousness of what she was allowing to happen.

'You're getting married!' she had protested, on a breathless sob.

'Yes.' He'd sounded cold, totally remorseless in comparison.

'Then don't you think you're being a little unfair?' she remembered saying, perplexed, hurting to think he could simply use her and then walk away.

'Unfair?' He looked as though he didn't fully understand. 'Unfair to whom?' he queried.

'Well, to me. Her…' she uttered, shaken by his total lack of morals. But he merely shrugged.

'Not if I haven't asked her yet. And I haven't,' he surprised her by saying then. 'I only said I was thinking about getting married. There is a difference. Whether I do or not depends on you.'

'On me?' She wasn't able to follow, so taken aback was she by this sudden turnaround of events.

'Wise up, darling.' He laughed then, and told her the truth. Getting her to decorate his home had been the only way he knew to become part of her life without her running away from him, and he laughed again later, when she accused him of trapping her by deceit.

'No,' he said softly. 'I only wanted to show you what you were too afraid to realise you wanted.' But this was only much later, among the soft, virgin folds of the duvet where he had made her his.

One week later, he slipped an engagement ring on her finger, and they were married within six more. Three months after that she was expecting Matthew, passionately happy and content…

Now she blinked angrily at the tears that stung her eyes, glancing down at her watch.

Blast Jarrad Mitchell! she thought. Matthew was all that mattered to her now! And, grabbing her keys, she darted out through the French doors to collect him, as though just the whisper of his father's presence in her life again could have the power to spirit the little boy away from her.

Tony telephoned the next morning. He had tickets for the theatre that coming Saturday, he told her, given to him by a grateful client.

'I thought you might like to go,' he suggested, and Kendal could imagine him sitting there behind his disorderly desk with his pleasant face hopeful—though not unduly concerned—beneath his wiry and equally disorderly brown hair.

She tottered on the brink of accepting when he told her the name of the show, but only for a moment. She didn't want an involvement with Tony—or with anyone else for that matter—to which a date like that might inevitably lead. But, more importantly, and the main reason she resisted his offer—which was the reason she gave—was because she had left Matthew once too often during the past week— and this coming weekend she was determined that nothing was going to come between them.

The sight of him tugged at her heartstrings as she watched him put the last of three bricks on top of the others in a precarious little tower on the worn, though serviceable carpet, then clap his hands with a delighted squeal.

She was going to spend every second alone with her son. And if she did take this job in the States, she ruminated— found herself a nice place to live—she might eventually be able to work from home and employ a part-time nanny for Matthew so that they would never really need to be parted. Until then, though, she was forced to leave him as she had this week. And next week wasn't looking much better...

It wasn't so much that that put an uneasy look in her eyes as she replaced the receiver after speaking to Tony. It was the thought of Friday week. Next Friday, when Jarrad would be round to fetch Matthew for the afternoon, his insistence that she go with him...

The phone, when it shrilled again, startled her so much that she almost spilled the warm milk she had been pouring into Matthew's beaker.

'Kendal?'

Relief and something else swept over her. What was it? Disappointment? Surely not! she thought, amazed, silently berating herself for the way her voice shook when she answered her sister's call.

'Are you all right?' Chrissie sounded baffled. 'You sound…well…out of breath.'

Kendal forced a laugh. 'Probably because I rushed to answer the phone,' she bluffed, hoping Chrissie wouldn't guess how much she was letting Jarrad get to her after all these months!

'I'm going away for a few weeks! That's what I'm ringing to tell you! I'm going to tour Europe! Isn't it exciting? And I'm leaving in the morning!'

'What? How? Who with?' Kendal pressed, almost equally infected by her sister's tangible excitement.

There was a brief pause. And then Chrissie surprised her by responding with, 'Ralph. He telephoned yesterday—late last night! You know he's been working for that firm abroad? Well, he's coming back—but he's taking a few weeks' holiday first. And, oh, Kendal! He's asked me to go with him! For us to get back together! He said he regrets all that's happened and wants us to try and sort things out!'

'That's great!' Kendal could almost have wept with the emotion that welled up inside her. Chrissie deserved happiness. She only hoped that this time things would work out for her and Ralph.

'I'm sorry to be going. At a time like this when… Well, you know…when you might be getting so much hassle from Jarrad…'

'Don't be silly,' Kendal was quick to reassure her. Whatever Jarrad cared to throw at her, she could handle it! she assured herself, though with more rebellion than conviction.

'And you won't hold it against Ralph if he does come back?' That excited voice of Chrissie's couldn't hide the smallest suspicion that her older sister might harbour some grudge towards Ralph for running out on Chrissie as he had. But why should she? Kendal reflected. It was only the strain of the situation into which Jarrad's insensitivity had plunged them that had split them up. Ralph hadn't been premeditative or ruthless. Nor had there been another woman…

'Of course not,' she exhaled, the memory of Jarrad's betrayal making it difficult to keep her voice steady. And, wishing fervently suddenly that she could protect her little sister from the weight of anything like the misery of her own heartache, she uttered, 'Oh, Chrissie, be careful!' She couldn't bear the thought of her sister getting hurt a second time.

'Don't worry,' Chrissie chided emphatically, but Kendal always did—and not without good cause. Chrissie's volatile nature meant that she didn't always deal with situations in the positive way she should, and Kendal hadn't forgotten how desperate her sister had been when Ralph had left her last year—nor the attempted overdose that, mercifully, had failed.

They spent a few moments chatting then, with Kendal offering to take time off to drive her sister to the airport, but Chrissie wouldn't hear of it. After she had hung up, Kendal felt remarkably depressed.

She was happy for her sister, of course she was. But the thought of a few weeks without her wasn't a prospect she was looking forward to very much. She was glad, though, that she had managed not to let her own anxieties about Jarrad trickle through, because she didn't want to worry Chrissie, and she was relieved that she had managed to send her sister off with almost as much enthusiasm as Chrissie herself.

Chrissie rang Kendal briefly from the airport the following afternoon. Then every day for most of the following week Kendal kept herself occupied with Matthew and her work for the Arkwrights, popping round once or twice to water Chrissie's multitude of plants.

As the week progressed, though, she found herself growing more and more agitated, and by Thursday she was uncustomarily snappy. She knew it all centred around the fact that the following day was Friday, when Jarrad would be calling round.

Dropping Matthew off with the dependable, indispensable Valerie, she spent the morning in a turmoil, wondering what excuse she could give to Jarrad about not accompanying him back to the house with Matthew.

She couldn't face going there. Perhaps, she eventually decided by way of a compromise, she might suggest they went out somewhere—the three of them. Somewhere where there were people, where she wouldn't have to be alone with Jarrad. The power of his physical attraction—and after all he had done—still terrified her, and she realised that she was still much too vulnerable to go anywhere with him alone.

He arrived grossly and unexpectedly early, just as she came off the phone from making a succession of futile calls about some wall covering she was trying to get hold of for the Arkwrights, at the end of a morning that had seemed to race by. It still wasn't time, though, for Valerie to bring Matthew back, as it had been arranged that she would do so at two o'clock, and Kendal started as Jarrad strode in without knocking, just like the last time, through the open patio doors.

'You're early,' Kendal accused, the telephone clattering back onto its rest evidence of the aggravating morning she had endured.

'I wouldn't dream of incurring your wrath by even daring to presume to be, darling,' he murmured, the very sight of him taking her breath away.

He had obviously come straight from the office, the immaculate silver-grey suit and white shirt enhancing the tan that gave a vitality to those already healthy features. She wondered if he had been on holiday somewhere with Lauren, then told herself she didn't care.

'Well? Are you both ready?'

So he expected her to drop everything, did he? Just like that!

A toss of loose red waves signified her agitation. 'Do I look it?' she asked crisply, and felt his gaze tug over her uncombed hair and flushed features, then move disconcertingly to the rather gaping V of her cotton shirt.

'You'll do,' was all he said drily, and then, with a glance towards the lounge door, 'Where's Matthew?'

Kendal caught her breath. Of all the nerve…!

'He isn't back yet. I—'

'Back from where?' he interrupted, his tone inexorable. 'The minder's again? Or have you palmed him off on your little sister this time?'

'I don't *palm him off* on anybody!' she threw back, furious. She loved Matthew. More than anything. Anyone! 'And, if you must know, Chrissie's gone away with Ralph! They're back together! So you see, Jarrad, you didn't quite succeed in destroying them completely—even though you tried! And, yes, Matthew's with Valerie,' she finished more calmly, in spite of the daunting menace in his face that told her he didn't like being reminded of what his cruel actions had done to her sister's marriage.

With those black brows drawing together, all he simply said was, 'What—still?'

'Yes, still,' she said pointedly, looking up at him with challenging defiance. It was her business how she ran her life! 'I told you. You're early. I asked her to have him back here by two.'

'Then where is he?' He frowned down at the thin gold watch gleaming against the dark hair of his tanned wrist. 'I make it nearly twenty-five to three.'

Puzzled, Kendal glanced down at her own watch. 'I make it twenty past one…'

'Then one of us obviously needs a new timepiece,' he remarked, with both hands coming to rest on the table.

Kendal's frown deepened and, jumping up, she ran into the lounge, sending an anxious glance towards the video clock.

Fourteen *thirty-three*? Jarrad was right! So where in the

world was Matthew? Valerie? She was already over half an hour late!

Kendal felt the tension building with the fear inside her. Had she had an accident? The woman was a mother herself—highly recommended by another young mum Kendal had worked with—and was nothing if not reliable. 'She's never, never been late...!'

'Never except today.' She hadn't realised she had spoken aloud until she heard that harsh, sceptical drawl from the doorway, and she swung round, green eyes ablaze.

'I suppose you think I arranged this deliberately just to antagonise you?' Anxiety made her snap as she brushed past him, heading straight for the phone on the table.

'To antagonise me, perhaps not,' he accepted. 'To stop me seeing my son, I wouldn't, however, put anything past you.'

She ignored his remark, tapping out the number of her child minder's home just as the front doorbell rang.

'So she's condescended to bring him back!' Jarrad's mood was black as he strode out of the room, taking it on himself to answer the door.

'*Mr* Mitchell?' It was a man's voice, cold, very official, drifting along the hallway, and Kendal dropped the phone, feeling the grip of icy fingers around her heart.

'Yes.'

'What is it? What's wrong?' Already she was at the door beside Jarrad, facing the young policeman—and the policewoman—standing there, looking serious, on the doorstep. 'There's been an accident!' Oh, God...!'

'No, Mrs Mitchell.' The man looked at her gravely. 'It is Mrs Mitchell, isn't it?'

Numbly, she could only nod.

'For heaven's sake, get on with it, man!' Jarrad prompted impatiently, looking grim yet in command too, still in control, even in this situation.

The policeman visibly tensed, obviously recognising the authority in the older man, though his training wouldn't allow him to be browbeaten. 'Do you think we could come in, sir?' he said, with the sort of deference everyone paid to Jarrad Mitchell.

And then, somehow—Kendal wasn't sure how—they were sitting in the lounge, and all she was aware of was Jarrad standing there beside her, his hard, clipped voice demanding, 'Well? Are you going to tell me what's happened to my son?'

CHAPTER THREE

SNATCHED!

Kendal stared at the small circular brown stain on the worn carpet that seemed to be swimming in front of her eyes. There had been endless questions, and more police, the second lot more interrogative than the first.

But they had all gone now, leaving her to cope with the numbing realisation of what had happened.

Matthew kidnapped. Abducted. Her little baby snatched away while he was supposed to have been in Valerie's care, when she had thought he was safe, secure...

'Here.'

She stared sightlessly at that familiar masculine hand holding the thick glass tumbler in front of her, at the dark hair feathering the tanned wrist.

'Drink it,' he ordered. 'It will make you feel better. Or at least put some life back into you.'

Because she had nearly fainted, she remembered—almost collapsing from the shock when the policewoman had told her, and she had recovered herself to feel Jarrad's arm supporting her, his voice murmuring soft assurances. Empty assurances, she thought, because, of course, what could he do?

She took the glass he thrust at her now and drank, coughing at the burn of brandy on her throat.

Mrs Humphries, the police had said—referring to her child minder—was still in shock, distraught, unable to comprehend how it could have happened. Matthew had been playing in the front garden, with the gate locked, she had told them. Her back had only been turned for a moment, but when she had looked round again he was gone.

But how could he be gone? Kendal agonised. Her baby stolen? Taken away. Just like that. True, it was only a low gate, but Matthew was shy of strangers, and if someone had tried to lift him over he would have screamed...

'That's better,' she heard Jarrad say as she took another sip of the burning spirit. 'That's my girl.' And as he took the glass from her she thought how soft his voice was, surprisingly gentle. She hadn't heard him speak to her like that in over a year.

'What are we going to do?' A ton of granite seemed to be pressing on her chest, and the eyes she turned to his were sore and puffy, their dark anxiety almost an entreaty to him, as though he had powers that she didn't, as though he could make everything all right.

'We'll have to wait and see what the police come up with.'

He turned away from her, dumping her glass down on the narrow bay windowsill, and stood, staring out at the ash tree in the colourless communal front garden, its branches swaying today in a keen breeze.

'Wait and see!' Propelled by a new surge of adrenalin, Kendal sprang to her feet, coming halfway across the room. 'I can't just sit here and wait while someone's out there doing heaven knows what with my son!'

The near hysterical note in her voice brought him swinging round to face her.

'And isn't he my son, too?' he breathed, those restrained emotions carving deepening grooves into that inexorable face.

Kendal caught her breath as a shuddering sob threatened to choke her. 'Yes, but you don't love him as much as I do!' the intolerable torture made her cry.

'Don't you ever—' He cut short his sentence and the sudden move he made towards her, and his lips compressed into a tight, disciplined line. 'Do you think,' he said in a quietly controlled voice then, 'that just because he wasn't sharing my home you have the right to suppose I somehow loved him less?'

A door banged somewhere else in the house, and somewhere above them someone ran a tap. Normal, everyday sounds in someone else's normal, everyday existence that barely impinged on Kendal's tortured mind as her face twisted in sudden horror.

What was he saying? 'Don't do that!' Her fingers clawed at the front of her shirt. Dear God, how could she bear it?

'Do what?' Bafflement etched lines around those narrowing blue eyes.

'Relegate him to the past!'

'Don't be ridiculous!' She could see the tension in him, in the way his hands balled into fists at his sides and unclenched themselves again. 'It was just a manner of speech.'

Of course it was, she told herself, trying not to allow herself to become hysterical.

'Perhaps if he'd been with you as he should have been this whole damn thing might not have happened!' he rasped, blaming her as he had blamed her for everything, she thought through her lacerating pain—for her paranoia, as he'd called it, over him and Lauren, for working, for leaving him, and now for the loss of her child.

Much later she would decide that it was probably only his own intense anguish that had prompted him to say it, the helplessness he felt over Matthew's disappearance. He was angry and frustrated at being unable to do anything, when normally all he had to do was snap his fingers for the world to accommodate his wishes. But at that moment she couldn't take the weight of any more blame when her own guilt was threatening to crush her.

She kept thinking that if she hadn't thought it so important to work today Matthew would still be here now. That if she hadn't been on the phone about that wall covering for so long, which seemed so unimportant now, then Valerie might have been able to alert her sooner before she had even contacted the police, and she might have been able to have done something—anything! She didn't know what. She only knew, with an overwhelming certainty, that the blame rested squarely on her own shoulders.

'Perhaps if you'd put your wife and child first—hadn't played around with Lauren—he might be here now,' she nevertheless couldn't help retaliating bitterly, because no one was blaming him. Even the detective constable, having determined the state of their marriage, had asked her frankly if she had taken her baby somewhere so that she wouldn't have to allow his father access—although no one had asked the same question of Jarrad, or if they had she hadn't heard them, although the man *had*, in the end, apologised. *Apologised!*

'You were the one insisting I keep Matthew in this country—threatening to take him away from me if I didn't! Perhaps you arranged this...' What had started as just a wounded reprisal now became a staggering possibility. Hadn't she said she was going to fight him? That would have meant a fierce battle through the courts. So what if he'd decided to save them both the trouble?

'Perhaps you arranged it with your oh, so clever Ms Westgate to take him away! Is she any good with children? After all...'

Censure narrowed her long green eyes as she went on, verbally lashing out, hurting herself, hurting him. 'No one would suspect *you* of anything like that, would they, Jarrad? The respected businessman. It might be acceptable for a man of your means and influence to stoop to wanting two women in his bed—but never baby snatching. Who would suspect you?' Her voice was rising by the second. 'The high and mighty Jarrad Mitchell stooping to kidnapping his own—'

'Stop it!'

With one stride he had closed the distance between them, his fingers digging in as they grasped her roughly by the shoulders.

'Why?' She contested, oblivious to the reason for the harrowing shadows across his face, feeling only her own pain, her own relentless guilt. 'Can't you bear hearing the truth? Can't you take what you—?'

'I said that's enough, Kendal!'

He was shaking her now, churning up pain and anger and remorse into a bubbling well of misery, until it flowed out of her on a shuddering gasp and she collapsed against him in a helpless outpouring of emotion. While she had half convinced herself that he had taken Matthew, she could at least assure herself that her baby was safe and, for that reason alone, she realised, she had been almost hoping that he had.

One arm across her shoulders, the other against her back, he held her gently, saying nothing, so all she was aware of as her sobs began to subside was the tick of his wristwatch close to her left ear and the patter of some paper litter being blown by the brisk breeze along the street.

A long time later, when her crying had ceased altogether, he said quietly, 'Come on.'

She turned a red, blotchy face to his as that supportive arm around her shoulders turned her gently towards the door.

'Where are we going?'

'Home.'

'Home?' Bewilderment brought her fine dark brows together, and then realisation sent a swift dart of panic through her, causing her to draw back.

'You're not staying here alone,' was all he said determinedly, feeling her resistance.

'But I have to,' she countered adamantly. 'What if Matthew comes home? What if someone brings him back?'

'Just like that?' Jarrad's mouth twisted in firm dispute, but when he spoke again he seemed to pick his words carefully, weighing everything he said. 'Do you think that's very likely? If this isn't…' He paused, seeming unable to go on. Then, 'You know what that policeman said,' he

reminded her. 'That someone may have taken him to try
and get some sort of ransom. If that's the case, then they'll
know where to come.'

Of course. Jarrad Mitchell was extremely wealthy, and a
lot of people knew it. And anyone who might have been
planning this, watching her movements, would realise from
this flat in this less than salubrious area, and the modest
little car she drove, that she had no real means of her own.

'But if you're worried…'

He strode into the other room, over to her answering
machine, and, flicking up the cover, put a new message on
the tape with his own number where she could be reached.

'That should take care of it,' he said, snapping the cover
down before going over to secure the patio doors he had
closed when it had started growing chilly earlier. 'And now,
Kendal…' His tone brooked no resistance as he came
across to where she was standing in the doorway. 'You're
coming back with me.'

And that was that, she thought, knowing it was point-
less—even if she hadn't been too exhausted—to argue.

Her heart was in her mouth as Jarrad turned off the road
in the exclusive London suburb, bringing the gleaming
black Porsche through the familiar gates and to a standstill
at the end of the short drive.

So often had she imagined this homecoming, she
thought, feeling the lump catch in her throat as she looked
up at the elegant Tudor-style house he had had built for
her; imagined it, but only in her wildest dreams. And it had
always been a moment of immense joy when she ran into
his arms again, and nothing that had happened in the past
had really happened at all. Not this ordeal, when the memory of the way she had run from here that last time punctured
wounds she knew now had never even started to heal, on
top of the nightmare of all that had happened today—with
Matthew.

Matthew! Oh, dear heaven, please let him be safe…

'Come along.'

She was grateful for Jarrad's strong arm as he helped her out of the car and led her up the low steps, opening that familiar oak door.

It could almost have been yesterday when she had walked out of here, she thought as she absorbed, rather than noticed the familiarity of things—the carved, curving balustrade at the foot of the stairs, the scent of the beeswax that Teeny always used, the way the evening light shone through the dining-room window opposite, striking fire from the polished silver. Everything was the same. Everything—except for one. There were no infant sounds to break the deathly silence.

'You look all in.' Jarrad had closed the door and was studying her with dark, solicitous eyes. 'And you haven't eaten a thing all day.'

'What does it matter?' she asked flatly, still clutching the little blue bear she had grabbed out of Matthew's room before she had left the flat. His favourite...

Jarrad made a disapproving sound through his nostrils. 'It matters to me.'

Did it? How strange that she couldn't seem to care.

'You've got to get something inside you,' he said, as though he were reprimanding a child. 'Even if it's only a bowl of soup.'

Kendal's mouth twisted, her stomach rebelling at the mere suggestion of food. 'I couldn't.'

That strong face took on a determined cast. 'Nevertheless, you're going to. I have to—'

The sudden ringing of the hall phone interrupted whatever he had been going to say, and Kendal's heart pounded in anticipation as Jarrad beat her to it, his urgent response as he picked it up strung with the same expectant hope that was burning through her.

'No, I'm afraid my wife isn't up to answering any more questions tonight.'

It was the police again and he was fending them off,

protecting her from a barrage of further questions. Her shoulders sagged with the agony of her dashed hopes. They hadn't found her baby...

'I can't sit around here waiting. I've got to go out and look for him!' She had scooped up the keys he had discarded on the telephone table and was halfway to the door by the time he had dropped the phone.

'Don't be ridiculous!' He had reached her in two strides. 'And where the devil do you think you're going to begin looking?'

She pushed away the hard, restraining hands that gripped her shoulders, her features contorted with rebellion.

'I don't know! I only know I have to! If I sit around here, not knowing what's happened to him, I'll just go mad!'

'Kendal!'

Strong fingers caught her wrist as she would have taken flight again, their dark strength tightening around her pale skin.

'Please don't stop me, Jarrad.'

'I can't let you do it, Kendal.' He gave no heed to the supplication in her voice, her face. 'I can't let you drive around in the state you're in, even if we had the foggiest idea of where to begin looking.'

How could he sound so cool, so rational, she wondered, when she was being driven insane wondering what might be happening out there to Matthew? Imagining him being without the people who cared about him. Perhaps alone and frightened. How could he, unless he didn't care about his child? Unless...

She dammed the flood of wild thoughts that were pounding through her brain again before they could get a serious hold on her. She had to keep her head. Stay as calm—or rather as controlled—as he appeared to be.

Get a grip on yourself. From somewhere she managed to find a small reservoir of strength within herself, and she closed her eyes with the effort, taking a deep breath.

Even though he had been wearing that light suit all day, Jarrad scarcely looked ruffled while she…she felt clammy and cold.

'I'm going to take a shower,' she murmured, opening her eyes at last.

She didn't feel like it. She didn't feel like doing anything, but she had to force herself into mundane, ordinary things because she knew that if she didn't she would go crazy.

'You're sure you're up to it?' He regarded her pale, strained features, her matted and lank red hair, the weary slump of her shoulders, and he grimaced.

'No.' She breathed an unconscious little sigh as he released her. 'But I'm going to anyway.' And when she saw the doubt in those penetrating blue eyes she uttered feebly, 'Don't worry. I'm not going to collapse on you again, if that's what you're thinking. I can cope. I've got to.'

Something flared in his eyes. Something she had seen before. And she realised as she turned away towards the stairs that it was admiration. Admiration, as when she'd told him that she was going to fight him—fight him to try and stop him taking Matthew away…

With her face upturned to the fierce, unremitting jet of the shower, Kendal felt the warm flow cascade down over her body, letting the water blind her, trying to drown her misery, losing herself in the simple mundanity of showering. Only it wasn't simple, it was a tremendous effort. And, when eventually she switched off the jet, watched the water swirl away over the ice-green marble, she felt totally spent, stepping out into the cool luxury of the bathroom with legs like lead, only to discover that there was just one small towel on the rail.

Using it to absorb the excess moisture from her dripping hair, she stood there for a moment, wondering whether to call out to Jarrad—which she was decidedly loath to do—

or simply trip along to the *en suite* bathroom in the master bedroom at the end of the wide landing.

Plumping for the latter, she wiped herself down roughly with the damp towel and tiptoed along to the main room.

She deliberately avoided looking at the enormous bed recessed between the luxurious white wardrobes, but hurried through the archway into what had used to be her dressing room, flanked on one side by further matching wardrobes and leading into the bathroom.

'Have you finished yet?'

Jarrad's deep voice drifting through the bedroom made her swing round, startled, so that all she could do was back away further into the dressing room as he strode in.

He seemed to catch his breath, his face and body going rigid as his gaze swept over her smooth shoulders and naked breasts, still dewy from the shower, then lifted to her disconcerted features, framed by the damp-darkened tendrils of her hair.

'I—I came in to get a towel,' she stammered. 'There wasn't one in the main bathroom.'

'No, I've just put some in there,' he said hoarsely. 'I'm afraid I grabbed the others this morning on my way out to the gym. Teeny usually replaces them, but she's having a couple of days off.'

So he still worked out in the mornings.

'Thanks. I was going to call you…' Her voice trembled with the lie, because despite everything she was too aware of the gaping chasm that existed between them for her to be standing here naked in front of him like this.

'Liar,' he breathed softly. 'You would have dressed wet before you'd condescend to risk me seeing you like this, wouldn't you?' he asked, those piercing eyes too shrewd, far too sagacious. 'This is much too intimate, isn't it? Isn't that why you chose to shower in the main bathroom instead of in here?'

He was right. She had always preferred to use this room's larger and more luxurious double shower, and hadn't today because, as he had so correctly assessed, it was far, far too intimate, the memories of when they had taken showers together still too vivid...

Discomfited, she brushed past him. She couldn't cope with this. Not tonight. She'd use one of the towels he'd said he'd put in the other room. But even before she had reached the bedroom everything she had been through that day seemed to culminate in a sudden bout of dizziness and, swaying, she grabbed the wall of the archway, lowering her head with a small, involuntary groan.

'What the...?'

Suddenly a large, fluffy bathsheet was being thrown around her, soft and warm, warm as the arm that came diagonally across her shoulder, drawing her back against the hard, supporting strength of Jarrad's body.

'Are you all right?'

He had discarded his jacket and tie since coming in earlier, and Kendal's breath caught at the unsettling warmth of him beneath the short-sleeved silk shirt, at the muscular arm that lay across her breasts.

She merely nodded, however, grateful to be able to lean against him for a few moments.

'I'm all right.' Her voice was strung with tension as, recovering, she started to pull away.

'No, you're not.'

She was scarcely aware of him lifting her up and carrying her through to the bedroom, only of leaning against that supporting shoulder as he rough-dried her hair with another towel he must have grabbed from the rail, sitting there beside her on the bed.

Like a child, she thought, with something welling up excruciatingly inside of her as she thought of Matthew. Oh, Matthew!

She hadn't even realised Jarrad had moved away until the bed depressed and he sat down again, until the hair-drier, which he must have found in one of the drawers of the dressing table she had once thought she was choosing for another woman, suddenly buzzed into life. She must have forgotten it when she'd left—the thought was barely coherent—or perhaps it was one of Lauren's...

'You never used to do this,' she felt she needed to remind him, needing to say something before she broke down from the double dose of torture she was suddenly experiencing, the cold, indescribable numbness.

He didn't answer, his actions economical as he suddenly flicked off the drier and laid it aside, and then, before she realised it, caught her limp legs and swung them up onto the bed, the sensual, king-size bed they used to share.

'Jarrad...' Her senses returned on full alert as she felt the bathsheet being removed from her aching body. 'This doesn't change things...'

The cool cotton of the duvet was being thrown over her.

'I can't stay here.' With an effort she made to sit up. 'I'm not sharing this with you...'

'Stay where you are,' he commanded. A restraining hand was on her shoulder, pressing her back down. 'If it isn't too offensive for you to be sharing the same roof with me, I'll be using one of the spare rooms.'

Kendal tried not to let her relief show too much. She didn't think she could take another verbal lashing on top of everything else.

'I—I didn't bring a nightdress,' she uttered, nevertheless feeling self-conscious lying there like that, there in the bed where he had carried her to ecstasy again and again, where they had first made love.

'I'm sure you can find one somewhere if your modesty's that important to you. You took very little with you,' he reminded her in a voice that flayed her with its coldness. 'Although it never seemed to worry you before.'

No, well... she thought, but couldn't bear to remember beyond that as he sat down again, bending to unplug the hair-drier from the three-pin point behind the bed, one hand resting on her pillow.

The lingering traces of his cologne with that other, more

indefinable scent of him were too evocative, that dark shadow around his jaw, the way he bent his head with that achingly familiar concentration in his face as he pored over a simple task—things that she remembered and had loved, and, oh, how she needed the comfort of familiarity!

Please hold me! she wanted to cry out. Take away this pain! This isolation!

But of course he was as much an enemy as the person who had stolen her baby. Almost as deadly because she didn't know what he thought, how he felt behind that frighteningly controlled façade. And on one hopeless surge of desperation, suddenly she was sobbing out, 'Are you sure you didn't take him, Jarrad? That this isn't all a ploy of yours? Just to punish me? Just to get me to come back?'

Still sitting on the bed, he brought his hands down on either side of her shoulders and his mouth twitched with something that was merely a gesture—devoid of all warmth—in the harsh, handsome structure of his face.

'Get some rest,' he ordered, as though the question didn't even warrant answering, and he got up then and went back downstairs.

Surprisingly, she managed to sleep sometime during the night, even though it was only for a couple of hours, and then only after it started getting light.

Some time during the evening Jarrad had brought her a lightly boiled egg and toast for supper, which she had left uneaten, one bite of the wholemeal bread seeming to stick in her throat as she'd tried to swallow, choked as she was with worry and desperation over Matthew.

It was the telephone, ringing beside the bed, that dragged her back to full consciousness and the new morning, and, momentarily, through a brain fogged with tiredness, she wondered why the sound should signal such an ominous feeling in her—until she remembered.

The ringing stopped after a few seconds.

Jarrad, she guessed, picking it up somewhere else in the house.

Through an upwelling of grief, her heart hammering, she leapt up in bed, reaching out, hand poised above the receiver.

Could it be the police? Had they found Matthew?

She couldn't wait until Jarrad came and told her. She had to know!

Quickly she snatched up the phone, her suspicions last night about Jarrad overridden now by the possibility that it might be someone making a ransom demand. Her heart seemed to stall with dread, every nerve placed on hold as, suddenly fearing the worst, she put the receiver to her ear.

'Oh, darling, I'm so sorry! What can I say?' Lauren Westgate's silken tones came as a total shock to her. They were the last person's she had expected to hear. 'Shall I come over?'

'No—no,' she heard him answer hesitantly, and she thought how weary he sounded. 'Kendal's here.'

'Kendal?' There was an element of surprise in Lauren's self-assured voice. 'Oh, of course…'

Well, what did she expect? Kendal thought, dumbfounded, as her brain started functioning again. She was only Matthew's mother! Or perhaps Lauren thought that didn't count!

'Look…can I do anything? I know how much he means to you.'

There was a pause before Jarrad spoke again. 'I don't know where the hell he is, Lauren!'

Like the guilty eavesdropper she was, Kendal heard that deep masculine voice crack, the cold, impassive stranger he had been with her the previous night belied by that one line of shuddering emotion.

'Oh, Jarrad! If there was only something I could do! If I could spare you this pain…'

Kendal put the phone down as quietly as she could. She didn't want to hear any more.

Matthew was hers. Hers and Jarrad's. But it was the other woman with whom he shared his grief. Not her. Not Kendal. Not his wife.

She had to stifle a sob, her breath catching from the agony of emotion in her chest.

Oh, Jarrad! How had things ever got this far? she wondered, torturedly, unable to bear his pain on top of the crushing weight of her own. Was it all a punishment for loving him too much? Some cruel trick of fate that had determined she lose not only her husband but her son as well?

She looked pale, the skin beneath her eyes appearing dark and bruised, when she came downstairs later wearing a clean, tie-waisted white blouse she had thought to bring with her from the flat with yesterday's light tailored trousers.

Teeny Roberts, having obviously returned from her short break, paused to express her regrets as Kendal met her coming through the hall.

'I don't know what to say, because there isn't anything I can say,' the woman sighed, sharing their distress.

'I know. Thanks, Teeny,' Kendal murmured, wondering, as she had done since her first meeting with Teeny Roberts, why the woman had ever allowed a nickname like that to stick when she was nearly six feet tall and generously proportioned with it. But she had been Jarrad's resident housekeeper for over ten years, since her husband had died and her daughter had married, having been a friend of his late foster mother, and Kendal knew she doted on him—more like a maiden aunt than an employee. It was evident now in the dubious way the woman viewed her as she said, 'It's good to see you again, Kendal.' And then went on to ask, 'How's your sister?'

'Fine,' Kendal supplied, remembering that Teeny had known about Chrissie's marriage break-up, as well as the other problems she had been having at the time. 'Things are looking up for her, but she's on holiday at the moment and doesn't know...' About Matthew, she'd intended to add, but couldn't because her voice faltered too much. She saw Teeny's dark head nod in sympathetic acknowledgement.

'Well, let's hope you won't have to tell her.' Teeny meant because they might find Matthew first. And this time Kendal nodded her understanding. As much as she loved her sister, she had enough to cope with without having to put up with Chrissie's hysterics when she found out as well.

'Thanks,' she murmured again, waving aside Teeny's offer to cook her some breakfast. 'I'll get something later,' she said.

Jarrad was standing by the wide bay window in the dining room, beyond the long, mahogany table, his body taut with a tension she could only guess at beneath his light casual shirt and trousers.

He was gazing out of the square-latticed panes, out over the lawn where the mallow bushes he had planted, with their delicate pink flowers, had grown considerably, she noted, during the past year. The beds of shrubs she had loved tending grew a little more wildly under the shadow of the massive cedar tree, but there was a bright array of Busy Lizzies at the end of the stepping-stones around the ancient sundial which Jarrad had purchased after he had had the extensive garden landscaped, before they were married.

'Oh, it's you,' he said with a cursory glance over his shoulder as he heard her come in, the brevity of his gaze cool, like his voice, as though what spark of feeling he might still have harboured for her had died even since yesterday. His son was gone. That was all that mattered.

'I'm sorry,' she whispered with a tremor in her voice as she came around the table, the rich wood catching the movement in its polished surface.

'For what?' He didn't even look at her, still standing there with his hands in his pockets.

'For the things I said yesterday.' It was difficult talking to his broad back. 'When I said you…had Matthew taken.'

He turned round then, and she noticed how tired he looked, wondered if he had even been to bed. 'What's brought this on?' he queried.

Kendal swallowed. What was the point of lying?

'I...heard what you said to Lauren.'

Something cynical tugged one side of his mouth. 'Still feeling the need to check up on me, Kendal?'

She deserved that; painfully she admitted it to herself.

'I thought it might be the police. I didn't think it would be Lauren!' she went on in bitter self-defence. And then, because his unrelenting need to hurt her succeeded so effectively, she added, 'I've got no interest in checking up on you. I don't care what you do!'

His face was expressionless as he surveyed her anguished features, the unusually dishevelled fire of her hair.

'Don't you?' he said, because he knew.

Oh, Jarrad, don't do this to me! her heart sobbed. *Not now!* But it was only her heart, because she had learned to conceal her feelings from him over a year ago. She didn't intend letting him see them ever again.

'You look awful,' he said then. And, as if to lessen the severity of the situation, keep them both sane, added, 'Particularly about the hair.' She could only guess at the effort that went into producing that barest indication of a smile.

'What did you expect?' she whispered.

There was anguish in his eyes, an intense and personal emotion that for a moment almost made her forget that promise to herself and run to him, put her arms around him and share her pain with him, take away some of his.

She didn't know what stopped her. Perhaps it was just the thought of Lauren ringing with that depth of feeling in her voice—not just the sympathy of one business colleague for another, but something much more intimate, a lover's feeling. Or perhaps it was the thought of her mother, lying there, cold and silent, her life snuffed out, indirectly because of a man's cruel betrayal.

She started, because the phone rang then, and this time it was the police.

CHAPTER FOUR

NOTHING. No news, the inspector had said. Had *they* heard anything? Could a couple of his people come round and talk to both of them again?

So had begun another day of endless questions. Endless wondering. Endless torture. And by the end of the day they were no nearer to finding Matthew than they had been the day before.

'You bore up well,' Jarrad praised softly as Kendal did little justice to a selection of sandwiches he had brought back from the supermarket, the first food she had had to eat since the barely touched bowl of cereal he had poured for her some time during the morning. She hadn't even looked at the lunch Teeny had cooked, and Jarrad had given the woman the rest of the day off. 'I know how hard it is for you.'

Did he? She didn't think he could begin to. Oh, perhaps he understood something of her torture; he was Matthew's father after all. But he hadn't been there during the past year when the little boy had woken up crying, when he had laughed and held out his arms in trusting, warm affection, when he had slept, nuzzled against her breast. How could he understand completely, she thought, this agony that tore through her as surely as if her son had been wrenched from her very womb?

'I just wish there was something,' she breathed, pushing the plate with her nibbled sandwich away from her. 'Something to hold onto.' It had been like living a nightmare for the past two days. She was half crazed with hope every time the phone rang, but each call had brought only disappointment and deepening anxiety, each hour a week as they waited for a ransom demand that never came.

'If it isn't a kidnapping—not your money they're after—what, then?' Kendal whispered, feeling as though she were suffocating from the effort not to break down all over again, afraid that if she did start crying she would never be able to stop, that the next time she would never, ever recover.

'Don't talk like that,' he advised sharply, and got up, picking up the plates and tossing the unwanted sandwiches into the bin, stacking the plates in the dishwasher.

Perhaps it was his way of dealing with things, she thought—carrying on as usual, being positive, refusing to think about the worst. Or perhaps, like her, he couldn't bear to…

Unable to sit there, too afraid to speculate, she longed for something to do that would keep her from thinking. Carrying on with her job, however, was out of the question at the moment. She needed what reserves of energy she had to stop herself from going under, needed what strength she had to keep reassuring herself that Matthew was going to be all right, that her baby was going to be found.

Dragging the cloth from the kitchen table and folding it into a drawer, she wandered into the adjoining utility room and saw Jarrad's black sports bag, which he must have retrieved from the boot of the car and tossed there some time during the day.

It still contained the damp, creased shorts, socks and towel that he had obviously used the previous day at the gym, and like an automaton she unpacked the bag and began piling the contents into the washing machine.

'Just because you're here, I wouldn't want you to feel it necessary to perform any wifely duties.'

Jarrad, coming in, startled her, causing her to drop one of his thick white sport socks onto the vinyl floor. She picked it up, throwing it into the machine with the other items, deciding against any obvious retaliation in response to his sarcastic remark.

'Is that what you thought it was? A duty?' she returned sadly instead, because anything she had done for him in the past she had done because she loved him. Not for any other reason. But of course she couldn't tell him that.

'Wasn't it?' was all he said, before reaching down for the emptied sports bag and swinging away.

Smarting, Kendal made her way upstairs after putting the machine into motion, pausing at the door to Matthew's old room.

She hadn't been able to bring herself even to put her head round the door since arriving yesterday evening, but now she pushed it open and looked inside.

Very little had changed. His cot with its blue coverlet still stood against one wall, and the suite of baby furniture was just as she had left it, with the full-sized ottoman behind the door. This was one room that they had decorated together, after she had known she was pregnant, and the memories came flooding back, the agony two-fold as the toy soldiers and trains and coloured balls danced before her eyes on the wallpaper she and Jarrad had so lovingly chosen.

She knew she was torturing herself even being in there, but she couldn't help herself. And now she placed the blue teddy she had brought with her last night in the little chair beside the cot, wondering with an intensifying emotion if Matthew was fretting for it, if he was able to sleep without it.

She wondered too where the collection of cuddly toys that had used to sit in that chair, and which she had had no room to take when she had fled from here in such a hurry, had gone. Perhaps Jarrad had finally given up hoping that she and Matthew would be back. That would be why there were so few of Matthew's old toys and personal possessions on view any more, she thought, looking around, wondering if he had sold them or simply given them away. Or maybe he had just put them in a cupboard, it struck her suddenly, and her compulsion to go across and open the little wardrobe revealed that he had.

Had he put them all away just to keep them free of dust? she wondered, the sight of the little toys stabbing her so sharply that she quickly closed the door again before emotion overcame her. Or had he simply been unable to bear having them on display?

Telling herself that the Jarrad she knew wasn't capable of that much sensitivity, she retreated painfully from the nursery just as the phone started ringing.

Rushing into the master bedroom, she stopped in her tracks, holding her breath on finding Jarrad, already in there, swooping to answer it.

'Yes.'

He had dropped down onto the bed, sitting there in only the light trousers he had been wearing earlier.

He put up his hand as she raced round the bed, indicating that it was nothing to do with Matthew.

Disappointment speared her, but she stayed there anyway, that rush of blood through her veins leaving her weak, limp with crushed hope, so that all she could do was flop down beside him.

It was someone from the office—obviously ignorant of what had happened to Matthew, because the police had advised against making it public knowledge yet, not while there was still some likelihood of a ransom demand.

'What's going on up there? Can't the damn place function without me?' he demanded, because he wasn't attending the office while things were as they were. 'I thought I left perfectly clear instructions...' There was a pause while some lesser member of his staff probably made some stammering excuse, Kendal decided, almost feeling sorry for whoever it was on the line. Then, 'All right,' he said briskly, and absently she heard him offering the benefit of his valued advice, aware only of that perfectly enunciated English, the rich, smooth timbre of his voice.

It was one of the first things she had fallen in love with—

his voice, she remembered reluctantly, wondering if Lauren had fallen into the same helpless trap that she had; wondering, too, as she had been wondering since last night, why, if the woman and her husband were still lovers, there was not some evidence of Lauren anywhere in the house—in this room—because there wasn't.

'All right. I'll get back to you.' She snapped out of her moment's deliberation to hear him saying. But how could he work—not fall apart as she was doing—if he was under as much of a strain? she thought, amazed, and knew that, no matter how he felt, that was what had made him the success he was—that ability to direct and command and authorise, to keep going, whatever the cost.

'The office,' he told her unnecessarily, and she thought she saw him wince as he sat back after replacing the receiver.

'What is it?' She could see the furrow that knitted his brows as he reached up to grip his shoulder, flex the muscles in the rippling contours of his back.

'It's nothing,' he said dismissively, but pain still lined his face.

'Of course it's something,' Kendal persisted. 'What is it? Or are you too proud to admit you're human like everybody else?'

For a moment his features seemed to soften beneath the obvious physical discomfort.

'Is that what you think I am? Superhuman?' he drawled sardonically. 'Or what you imagine *I* think I am?' A wry smile touched that hard mouth so that she had to lower her gaze, and she felt more disconcerted when it locked onto the powerful structure of his chest with that covering of crisp, dark hair. And then, as though he didn't wish to plunge them into another unnecessary argument, he said, 'Everything locks up sometimes—across my shoulders. Here...' The groove in his forehead deepened as he massaged the offending area. 'It's as if my neck's in a vice.'

'Let me see.' That he was in pain was obvious, and

Kendal could see that his attempt at self-massage was clearly proving ineffectual.

'Can...can I do that for you?' she heard herself tentatively volunteering.

'You?' He was looking at her as though she had offered to fly him to the moon.

'Does that seem so strange?' she queried, losing confidence by the second. It hadn't seemed such an out-of-the-ordinary thing to her to want to help him. 'I don't like to see anyone in pain,' she added, feeling the sudden need to justify her reasons.

'Even me? The big bad ogre?' he taunted, although when she didn't respond he muttered simply, 'Be my guest.'

Kendal lifted a hesitant hand, swallowing as she regarded the muscular perfection of his back. He was beautifully bronzed, with the type of body some men worked hard to acquire and others only dreamed of possessing, and the thick black hair that curled intriguingly against his neck made her want to plunge her fingers into its dark mass...

'Well, what are you waiting for?' he asked rather impatiently.

The feel of his skin was like warm velvet to her fingers, the framework it clothed steel-hard and familiar. However, she ignored the disturbing memories, the sensations that touching him evoked, concentrating on getting to the point of his pain, her hands working with as much dedication as she could muster.

'It would be best if you lie down,' she suggested at length, finding it awkward to apply any real pressure sitting beside him at such an awkward angle.

He complied, lying face down on the richly patterned duvet, the muscles bunching in those bare arms supporting his head.

'That's better.' Already she could feel his locked muscles loosening, feel the tension ebbing out of his powerful body.

'You don't know how much.' He gave a deep, gratified sigh. 'I'm not always lucky enough to have my own personal masseuse on hand. It's normally a case of just putting up with it. Learning to live with it,' he said.

'How long has it been tightening up like this?' Kendal enquired, surprised.

He made a sound down his nose as he considered her question. 'Seventeen—eighteen months.'

'Eighteen—?' Kendal broke off. So he must have suffered like this while they had been living together, although she hadn't been aware of it, and he had never mentioned it to her. Had never once complained...

'It only comes on if I'm under a lot of pressure.'

'Isn't that always?' She queried with a nervous little laugh because her hands were in danger of sliding down over that velvet back. Treacherously her fingers ached to feel again the power of his strong, masculine flanks—the tight, lean fitness of his waist—wanted not simply to massage away his pain but to caress and stroke...

He hadn't answered, and she heard the crack in her own voice as she added, 'And stress.'

'That too.'

And he was under enough of that at the moment, she thought with a flood of increased anguish as she thought of Matthew. They both were. Her hands stilled as she focused on a mental picture of his impish, beaming face, fought to stop herself from entertaining the silent, agonising question of whether he would ever be found.

'I keep remembering little things.' Her voice was a whisper, her face an agony of reflection as she gazed sightlessly at the firm, tanned flesh beneath her fingers. 'The various stages of his development. The first time he spoke my name—or rather, "mummy". His first step...'

The muscles beneath her fingers seemed to lock tight again, that riveting tension seeming to extend along his very backbone now.

'Unfortunately, I wasn't so lucky,' he rasped. 'I don't suppose you've ever considered for one moment what your running away deprived me of?'

She was stung by the coldness of his voice—because she had considered it—and what Matthew had been deprived of too—often, and with inevitable heart-wrenching regret. Kendal made to spring up, but swiftly Jarrad rolled round, catching her by the arm.

'Let me go!' She tried to pull away, the closeness of that exposed masculine chest suddenly too intimate, much too threatening.

'Why?' His mouth firmed into a thin, hard line. 'What's wrong, Kendal? Isn't it enough that you should deprive me of my son without imagining you could deprive me of what we had as well?'

Before she could even try to stop him he was pulling her down onto the bed, moving swiftly, so that now he was lying fully on top of her. She closed her eyes, groaning from the misery of her situation, her breath catching in her lungs from the threatening weight of him—because he only wanted to hurt her, lash out at her in anger, blame her for Matthew's disappearance, and yet he was equally blaming himself, she realised. She could tell that from the raw agony—if that was what it was—in his face, his voice.

A small sob left her lips, because whatever he did—dear heaven!—didn't she deserve it?

'Is that why you came in here like this—undressed?' she accused him nevertheless, with her green eyes glittering, feeling even now that unleashed sexual tension in him call to her, to that irrational part of herself that still wanted him. Because he hadn't come in here to answer the phone. He had already been in here when it had rung. 'Will it somehow make you feel better if you can take out your frustrations by taking me against my will?'

'Taking you…?' His lids were heavy with the weight of some deeply personal emotion. 'And make *you* feel better by giving you some real cause to hate me? Let you off so lightly for all the worry and humiliation you've caused me, Kendal?'

She wondered what worry and humiliation he was referring to, and guessed he meant her taking Matthew away from him. His voice was controlled, though, not the voice of a man who intended the most primeval of retribution, as he said, 'I'm sorry, darling, but I really hadn't intended to be that kind—to either of us!'

His swift withdrawal hurt more than the imagined abuse she had expected from him, his words ripping through her more than any sexual humiliation he might have thrust upon her.

'And, if it's of any significance to that affronted, suspicious little mind of yours, I came in here to get some clean clothes!'

The sound of a drawer opening bore testimony to that.

Of course. This was still his bedroom, she reminded herself, raising herself up on an elbow. She was the intruder here.

Reluctantly, she remembered how spent she had been the previous evening and how gently he had carried her in here, dried her hair and put her caringly to bed.

'Jarrad...'

He paused on his way out through the door, clean shirt over one arm—the way she had seen him so many times on his way to take a shower, after coming home from work, before going out for the evening, after those heady, unforgettable nights making love...

'What is it?' he asked, sounding almost uninterested.

Kendal felt a tightness in her throat. What could she say? I don't hate you? I...

She pulled up her thoughts with a sharp tug of mortifying self-debasement. Surely she couldn't still care for him, after all he had done? After all the resolutions she had made to herself over the past year to start afresh, never to become involved with a man like him again—with any man! Hadn't she learned her lesson—if not from her mother then from the depth of her own stupidity in loving at all?

'Nothing,' she lied, grasping at her floundering instincts for self-preservation. Because, of course, whatever else happened and whatever else he might do, it didn't alter the fact that he had made a mockery of his marriage vows with Lauren. She didn't know if they were still lovers, but they had been, and there was no going back on that.

'Nothing,' she uttered again when, for a moment, he seemed to hesitate, looked as though he was going to press her. But then he shrugged, thinking better of it and walked away.

Kendal didn't know how she got through the next couple of days. The ransom demand the police had suggested might be made for Matthew didn't materialise, and that led to everything becoming public.

There were announcements on the television, over the radio, newspapermen hanging around where they weren't wanted, waiting to pounce, hungry for information. How did she feel? What did they think had happened to their son? Had they employed anyone over the past couple of years who had been sacked and might be harbouring a grudge? Hadn't they been estranged when the little boy had been snatched?

Jarrad seemed to take it all in his stride, except for when they had been met with that last, very personal question. They were leaving for Valerie's to go over with the woman, yet again, every aspect of Matthew's disappearance—as though this time she might say something, anything, that might offer some clue as to who might have taken him. Then Kendal thought he was going to knock the man down.

'He's only doing his job.' Strangely, she had defended the recoiling young reporter as Jarrad had handed her into the car.

'And you think that includes prying into my family's personal affairs?' he had responded tersely, slamming her door closed. But she was beginning to realise that, curiously, despite his involvement with Lauren—whether it was over or still an ongoing affair—he seemed to want to keep the breakdown of his marriage from the outside world as far as possible. Perhaps, Kendal decided, he viewed it as the one failure in his life—and Jarrad Mitchell had never had any experience of handling failure!

Letters and cards flooded in as the news broke, well-meaning correspondence from colleagues and others she remembered as supposedly friends of both herself and Jarrad when they had been living together, but who long since had been content to let her go and had stayed true to Jarrad. Perhaps they preferred his sophistication, his ease of comradeship, to her awkward reserve—the reticent, retiring creature her insecurities and doubts had turned her into during those last, miserable days of her marriage. Or perhaps, she considered with a dart of wounded pride and bitterness at all he had put her through, they simply saw Jarrad as the injured party.

After opening the first one or two communications, though, she couldn't bring herself even to read their trite and carefully worded phrases, unable to cope with each fresh stab of anguish they unintentionally caused without the added reminder—when she saw how many were simply addressed to Jarrad—of what a sham her marriage had been.

There was a message from Tony too, on her answering machine, she discovered later in the week, when, after telling herself she had to do something about the work she had started for the Arkwrights, she had taken herself off to her flat. Tony, who, for all his carefree joking and happy-go-lucky personality, she realised, had obviously been too embarrassed by the situation to ring Jarrad's number and speak to her in person.

'Kendal...I'm sorry...' the message began, but she wound the tape on, her lips pressed tight against the now familiar piercing emotion as she steeled herself to carry on with normal things.

The swatches and colour charts were still where she had left them on the table that afternoon when Jarrad had called for Matthew. She had only been back with him once, briefly, to collect her car and some fresh clothes.

Absently she flipped over one or two of the sketches she had been working on initially. If it were possible for her to absorb herself in her work then perhaps there might be some measure of respite from this terrible suspense, she thought. But she knew she couldn't even begin to think about it at the moment. While she was under such a strain she could hardly do justice to the confidence that Jill and Peter Arkwright were placing in her ability as a designer. Even Jarrad was taking time away from the office. No one could expect them to function properly—carry on as normal—under the circumstances.

Tony sounded uncomfortable at first when she rang him back. Then he relaxed when he obviously realised that she wasn't going to start crying all over him, that all she seemed to want to discuss, in a quietly controlled voice, was the Arkwright job.

'You'll have to take it over. It's impossible for me to give my best at the moment,' she told him truthfully. And before he could offer any heart-wrenching sympathy she added quickly, 'You can reach me at this number if you need to contact me for any reason.' She repeated the number Jarrad had recorded on the tape before ringing off.

There was no important post. Jarrad came in every day to check if anything had arrived that might throw some light on Matthew's whereabouts, but nothing had. The least they could hope for—if money wasn't a factor, the police had said—was that he had been taken by someone who, for whatever reason, desperately wanted a child. Then they could at least hope that he might be being cared for.

She couldn't suppress a sob as she went over to the window and noticed the tumbler with what remained of the brandy that Jarrad had given her still standing there on the sill. There was a dead wasp lying in the shallow liquid.

'But he's so shy of strangers,' she uttered aloud, and then, to herself, He'll be miserable with anyone else.

Anyone but me or Jarrad or Valerie. And of course Chrissie.

Thinking of her sister made her suddenly realise that it had been over a week since she had been round to Chrissie's to check on the house, as she had promised to do during her sister's absence. Still, it was hardly surprising! she thought with a mental grimace. At the moment her whole life seemed to have been put on hold.

Nevertheless, summoning up the will, she drove over there straight from the flat, finding everything in order, watering the endless number of plants Chrissie had growing on every spare surface, and picking up the post.

There wasn't much—just a couple of circulars, something that looked like a bill and a brightly coloured postcard of some enviable location.

Casually she flipped it over, one glance at the less than familiar signature suddenly reminding her that this wasn't her home, or her mail, and swiftly she put the card in the letter rack on the telephone table with the rest of the unopened post to await Chrissie's return.

Checking upstairs, grateful for something to do, she switched on the light in the main bedroom to make the place look occupied, surprised because she was sure she'd already done so, and berating herself over not having done it on her last visit. She was always keeping on at her younger sister over her non-existent sense of security. She couldn't begin to imagine, however, how Chrissie would react when she discovered that her nephew had been kidnapped, and, for that reason alone, she was dreading Chrissie ringing.

Maybe she wouldn't, Kendal almost hoped as she was locking up. She hadn't heard from her sister since the morning she had left to join Ralph, although it was no less than she had expected. When Chrissie and Ralph had been away together in the past, they had never contacted anyone. Lost in each other, they admitted preferring to cut themselves off from the world while they were on holiday, abandoning newspapers, radio and television. So if news of Matthew's abduction even reached wherever they were, they probably wouldn't see or even hear it.

She only hoped, as she retreated down the path to her car, that at least *their* reconciliation might be working. Chrissie's emotions had been pushed to the limit when her marriage had broken up before, and Kendal didn't dare to speculate how her sister might react if things didn't work out this time. She didn't think she could cope with a distraught Chrissie and her own terrible anguish at the moment. In spite of that, though, as she put her key into the ignition, she realised she really was aching to hear from her sister.

Jarrad was coming out of his study as Kendal let herself in on her return, and one glance at his rigid features caused a painful tightening in her stomach.

'Any news?' A mixture of hope and dread tinged her voice.

He shook his head. 'Where have you been?' he demanded quietly, following her into the lounge, adding with biting cynicism, 'Visiting your boyfriend?'

His words rubbed like steel wool across Kendal's already frayed nerves and, dumping her bags down onto one of the settees beside the huge brick fireplace, she swung angrily to face him.

'No, as a matter of fact I've been to my flat—and Chrissie's!' she snapped, unable to help adding, 'Aren't you rather judging me by your own standards? If you don't believe me—look in there!' She threw open the huge carrier bag that revealed the swatches and charts she had brought in with her, before flopping down onto the sumptuous cushions of the comfortable settee.

'Thinking of working?'

It was a sneer, and she turned dark, wounded eyes in his direction.

'Do you really think I would? At a time like this?' she

exhaled, wondering how many more of his scathing remarks she could take on top of everything else.

Some unfathomable emotion seemed to pull his features taut for a few moments, and then he said softly, 'Well, at least something's more important than your job.'

Her breath caught in her lungs from even imagining he could contemplate anything else, but, before she could tell him so, he went on, 'So why did Beeson ring here? Is he missing you already?'

Kendal frowned up at him. 'He rang?' she queried, surprised, and, ignoring the hardening lines of his face she asked, 'Did he leave a message?'

'Hardly!' he breathed caustically. 'He was obviously not too keen on passing on his love through your husband.'

Kendal's heart sank. 'You didn't...?'

'Say anything out of line?' He knew exactly what she had been going to say, she realised, appalled by what he might have said to the other man. She supposed it was her own silly fault, though, for misleading Jarrad about him as she had. 'What do you think?'

Kendal shuddered. Tony might be a friend, but she didn't know how he would feel about being wrongly accused of consorting with her when nothing could be further from the truth.

'Did he want me to ring him back?' she asked unnecessarily, and when Jarrad didn't answer she jumped up and pushed past him, into the study.

She was aware of him in the doorway as she tapped out the number of Tony's office, but determinedly she forced herself not to turn around.

'Was that him? The strong and mighty king of TMS International?' Tony enquired as soon as she was put through to him. He was already aware that she was staying with Jarrad—though decorum, she guessed, prevented him from asking if it was to be a permanent arrangement. 'He certainly knows how to make a guy feel welcome! Possessive, isn't he?' he remarked. 'Not in what he said.

Just from the tone of his voice.' She could almost hear Tony whistling under his breath.

Well, thank heaven for that! Kendal thought with a sigh of relief, then went on to give him the number he wanted from the folder she had grabbed from the carrier before coming into the study.

'Perhaps you could collect all the paperwork and things,' she suggested wearily. 'Or send someone else round here to collect them.'

'I'll send someone,' he was quick to come back with, and Kendal wondered if it was because of his embarrassment while things were as they were, or because he didn't want to come face to face with Jarrad. A little of both, she suspected, coming off the phone.

'Satisfied?' she breathed, gathering up the folder she had tossed onto the long leather couch, about to flounce out of the study. His hands, though, were on either side of the doorjamb, and she stood stock-still in her tracks as she met the imposing barrier of his body.

'Nowhere near enough.'

That deep voice held a threat that made her wonder if he wasn't just referring to his suspicions about Tony, but to something more basic and disturbing.

Tension gripped her, and she bit her lower lip, feeling the stirrings of something dangerous beneath her fear as she faced him with a warning flare in her eyes.

'Why are you always prepared to think the worst of me?' he said, wise to the subtle language of her body.

'Perhaps because I know you so well, Jarrad,' she couldn't refrain from saying, with a challenging little lift of her head.

'Do you?' he asked softly.

There was scepticism in those two words, scepticism tinged with—

What was it? Sadness? Regret? Never! she thought self-derisively. Not Jarrad Mitchell!

As if she needed proof, his features were emotionless,

his feelings totally masked behind that rigid and practised self-discipline.

'I have to go out tonight. A business dinner,' he started to tell her then, as though that last unsettling little episode hadn't existed. 'TMS have been in negotiations with an American company for a new specialised software we brought out earlier this year, and it's a sixty-forty chance that they'll sign with us rather than a smaller company who can provide them with a similar package over in the States.

'Dwight Forster—their top man—has been over here for the past month, getting a feel for what TMS can offer, but he's flying home tomorrow and wants to talk things through once more with us before he'll commit himself one way or the other. I was hoping to be able to hand him over to Paul Lawrence—you remember, he's our new financial director—so that he could handle everything while things are so...'

For a moment some raw emotion lent a starkness to those strong features, exposing the inner man in all his puzzling complexity. 'Well, you know...'

Yes, she knew. Where Matthew was concerned he had room to feel.

'Anyway, because of all that's happened, I haven't had a chance to brief Paul fully yet—and, in any case, Forster's not looking too favourably on talking business with anyone but me.'

The mask was back in place. He was the tough, invincible businessman again. 'If I don't go, TMS could well lose the contract to its American competitor. And it isn't only for my benefit that I don't want that to happen—it's what a lot of individuals have worked hard for for months. Paul will be there—with his wife, as Forster's very social-minded. I know it's asking a lot, but I'd like you with me.'

Just like that?

'I can't.' Kendal looked up at him with wounded puzzlement. 'I can't go out socialising while my baby's out there somewhere—goodness knows where! I can't! And it

was a different tune just now, when you thought I was
intending to work!'

Jarrad dropped his hands to his sides, looking uncustomarily weary.

'Believe me, I wouldn't be going myself if it weren't
absolutely necessary,' he said on a long-suffering sigh, 'but
it is. Besides, I feel an evening away from this house might
do you some good—do us both good. Doing something—
anything—is better than just waiting around, waiting for
the phone to ring. I won't have you staying in on your own
for a whole evening without anyone for company. You'll
just work yourself up into a state if I let you. And Teeny
can't be with you. She's babysitting for her daughter tonight.' And when she just stood there shaking her head he
said, 'Kendal, I'm saying…please.'

He knew how to insist, allowing that courteous persuasion to clothe the barest hint of a command.

Anyway, perhaps he was right, she thought. Perhaps a
few hours out of this house might make her feel better,
although she doubted it.

'What sort of thing should I wear?'

Was that a glimmer of a smile that warmed his eyes? Or
relief? She wasn't sure.

'Just something smart. Nothing too formal,' he told her
casually as he stood aside and watched her go upstairs.

There were plenty of outfits to choose from. When she
had left, taking very little with her, she had abandoned a
large part of her wardrobe as well. Now she threw open
the doors of one of the tall white wardrobes and took out
practically the first thing she saw.

Dressing up was the last thing she felt like doing, so it
would have to do, she thought when she had showered.

It was a royal blue light silk two-piece, with a mid-thigh-
length top that flowed over the short, straight skirt which,
with the addition of a silver camisole, provided elegance
without too much formality.

Needing something to take the starkness off the jacket,

she spent a few moments sifting through the Italian jew-
ellery box that Jarrad had given her on her twenty-fourth
birthday. Reflecting his expensive and exquisite taste—like
some of the pieces it contained—it still sat on the dressing
table. It didn't, however, take her long to make up her
mind.

She chose her silver long-tail brooch—another present
from Jarrad, given to her on their honeymoon in Bermuda.
The graceful and delicate lines of the island's national bird
in flight complemented the striking silk as soon as she
pinned it on.

She could hear Jarrad moving around in the guest room
along the landing, and tried not to acknowledge how the
music that was drifting out from that room, playing softly
on the portable CD player he had taken in there, stirred her
as she went to find him.

He was in the adjoining shower room, tying his tie in
front of the mirror above the champagne-marbled basin.

'Will this do?'

As he turned and looked at her, at her perfectly flawless
complexion enhanced only by a touch of mascara and natural lip-colour, at the fiery silk of her loose hair and the
elegant outfit, words seemed to fail him.

'You look...beautiful,' he said quietly at length.

He didn't look so bad himself, with his black hair freshly
groomed and a pristine white shirt tucked into dark, well-
cut suit trousers which emphasised his tight, lean waist and
narrow hips. But he seemed reluctant to take his eyes off
her, and that steely regard made her catch her breath, made
her pulse beat a little too quickly.

'And *you've* cut yourself,' she noticed, relieved to be
able to draw his attention away from her when she saw the
small red nick at the side of his jaw.

'Oh?' He brought his hand across his chin, saw the tell-
tale evidence on his fingers.

'You've got blood on your shirt,' she commented.

'Have I? Where?' His mouth pulled at one side as he glanced down, trying to see it.

'Just below your collar.' She touched a less than steady hand to his chest. 'There.'

He groaned when he saw where she was pointing in the mirror.

'Shall I get you a clean one?'

'No,' he said. 'There's no time for that.'

'I could try and sponge it out for you,' she suggested. He looked hopeful. 'Could you?'

'I shan't promise anything.' Quickly she disappeared, returning with a small new triangle of sponge she had bought for make-up, and moistening it under the warm tap.

'You aren't usually so careless,' she admonished softly for something to say, too conscious of the warmth and hardness of his body as she began to sponge the small red stain from his shirt.

'No,' he agreed, and didn't need to say any more. He knew why. They both knew why. Behind that strong, masculine exterior he was fighting his own private battle for survival, trying to stay afloat amidst a sea of hell and agony over Matthew.

Above the evocative music that was still drifting in from the other room, she said, 'You should stick to the electric shaver.'

'Perhaps,' he said with an oddly sensual curve to his mouth, making her colour rise as she remembered how once she had told him that she liked a man using a wet razor, that it added something to his masculinity—and had consequently paid for it the very next time she had found him shaving in the *en suite* bathroom when he had chased her back into the bedroom and made love to her there and then, spreading shaving foam all over her body with his kisses.

She couldn't look at him as she dabbed diligently at the now gradually fading stain, not allowing her gaze to lift any higher than the level of his jaw. She could feel his breath stirring the hair against her temple. Hear it too, strong yet oddly shallow at times, as though he was inhaling her tantalising scent—because she still used Ysatis—the perfume he had bought for her that first Christmas that they had been together, and which he'd recognised instantly that day in his office. Or perhaps she was only imagining that irregular rhythm to his breathing over the soft strains of the repetitive, undulating theme that was still playing in the bedroom.

He used music, she remembered, just as she made use of an aromatic bath—to relax him after a hard day. Strong, classical stuff, sometimes poignant and stirring, like the type that was playing now.

'Couldn't you have played something else?' she demurred, her gaze still trained on the wet, transparent area of his shirt that now showed the dark tan of his flesh beneath.

'Don't you like it?' he enquired smoothly—too smoothly in the circumstances.

'Let's just say it wouldn't exactly have been my choice.'

'Not the *Canon*?' Through her lashes she could see his face displaying only mock innocence. 'I thought you liked Pachelbel.'

Which is why you're torturing me with it, she thought achingly, gasping as his fingers closed over the hand trying to redeem his shirt.

'The first time you heard it, I remember it reduced you to tears.'

Because it had moved her so much. And not just the music—*you*! her heart screamed, refusing to be silenced despite her clamouring desire to forget. Because they had been playing it in that restaurant the night he had given her that orchid, with his promise of undying love, the night they'd become officially engaged. And afterwards she had chosen the piece to be played in church—as her wedding music...

'That was the first time.' Determinedly she pulled her

hand free, aware that she had only been able to because he had allowed it. 'There,' she said, and this time her voice sounded decidedly shaky as she finished dabbing at his shirt. 'No one will ever know there was anything there.' And she meant it, turning swiftly away out through the door, so that he wouldn't see the emotion sparkling in her eyes.

CHAPTER FIVE

THE hotel to which Jarrad drove them was in fact a small stately mansion, still partly occupied by descendants of the family who had been living there for generations. It was an English gentleman's house, with views over acres of parkland, and a suitable setting to entertain an illustrious American, Kendal decided with a kind of numb cynicism.

A greying, fit-looking man in his fifties, there was an understandable air of solemnity about Dwight Forster, who arrived with his pretty, petite blonde wife at the same time as Paul and Diana Lawrence, and joined Jarrad and herself in the elegant lounge where pre-dinner drinks were being served, because, of course, they knew about Matthew—everyone knew.

'I feel I should speak for everyone here when I say how sorry we are to learn of the…ordeal you are undergoing at the moment, Kendal, and that I think it is very…brave and commendable of you to accompany your husband here tonight.' It was the American who was speaking to her so venerably after the introductions had been made and they were all seated around the long, low table. 'Both Virginia and I—and I'm sure everyone in my company back home—would like to convey our sincerest hopes that everything will resolve itself with the minimum of anguish to you all.'

Well, what else could he say? Kendal thought. No one knew for certain whether Matthew was dead or alive.

Through choking emotion she heard Jarrad offering a grateful but clipped response, speaking for them both, while she could only nod her head, thinking she would break down if she tried to utter a single syllable.

As she probably would have, she thought later, if she

hadn't felt the pressure of those strong fingers on her arm, felt Jarrad's enviable mental stamina supporting her—supporting them both—so that she was able from somewhere to find enough courage and strength of her own to face the evening ahead.

It might have been tolerable, she considered at some point, if Lauren hadn't arrived only minutes after Dwight Forster had delivered that little speech. She was looking as chic and as confident as ever, in a coffee-coloured silk trouser suit that contrasted well with her short, highlighted blonde hair. She wore pearls at her throat and matching large pearl earrings. Obviously cultured, Kendal decided, like the woman they adorned. Polished, practical, yet screaming of a sophistication that she herself sadly lacked. Perhaps it came with age, she thought without any intended malevolence, because Lauren was only a year or two younger than Jarrad.

Sitting on the low sofa beside him, Kendal tensed as Lauren came and sat down on the empty cushion on his other side, having first shaken hands with the Americans. She didn't seem to need an introduction to Dwight, having clearly met the eminent businessman in her capacity as sales director on previous occasions. From the man's almost imperceptible frown, as he looked from Kendal to Lauren and then back to Kendal again, she couldn't help wondering what he was thinking. That perhaps Lauren would have been more suited as Jarrad's wife? After all, they spoke the same language, travelled around a lot together, didn't they? Or had their relationship become as obvious to everyone else as it was to her? she thought harrowingly, with a dart of something like bitter jealousy arrowing through her.

'What are you doing here, Lauren?'

While the Forsters were exchanging pleasantries with Paul—a tall, very thin, mousy-haired man in his forties—and his dark-haired, rather shy wife, Kendal caught the question Jarrad posed to his colleague, and there was a definite undertone of annoyance in his voice.

'Well, what did you expect?' Lauren's smooth tones were low but unperturbed. 'You haven't been in the office—what with that conference you've been on, and then...everything else—and I desperately needed to see you. It didn't seem very...prudent to come to the house.'

'No,' was all Jarrad said flatly, and Kendal wondered if he regretted the constraints her presence was obviously putting on him as she considered to what extent Lauren's prudence stretched. Was she staying away purely out of a regard for their feelings? Or because she couldn't face seeing the man she clearly idolised sharing his home with his estranged wife?

Kendal didn't, however, catch what the woman said next, because Paul had grabbed her attention and was trying to include her—with tentative consideration—in the conversation. Everyone was treating her with consideration. Then the waiter arrived with the menus and the next fifteen minutes were taken up with selecting their various choices for the meal.

All except Kendal, who didn't want to be there, and who blindly ordered the 'chef's recommendation' for the evening and didn't realise, until she was seated at the pristine-clothed round table in the dining room, between Jarrad and his illustrious customer, and the meal was being served, that she had ordered guinea fowl which she didn't particularly care for.

But as she wasn't hungry anyway, what did it matter? she thought wretchedly. Although Jarrad had been right, she found herself deciding eventually. If she had stayed home alone she would very probably have gone mad!

As it was she did her best to make polite conversation with the amiable Dwight Forster, while the beautifully presented food—which she knew in other circumstances would have been wonderfully palatable—seemed to stick in her throat, and what she did manage to swallow tasted like sawdust.

'Relax.' For a moment, while the others were engrossed in a conversation about marketing concepts, she heard Jarrad's deep voice close to her ear. 'I know this has to be an ordeal for you, but you're doing splendidly.'

Doing splendidly! When her baby was out there…!

She sucked in her breath with the ravaging torture of not knowing, and felt the sudden warmth of Jarrad's hand on her thigh beneath the table, burning through the soft silk of her skirt. As if things weren't bad enough, having to drag herself here in the first place, without being forced to endure Lauren Westgate's company as well!

'So are you,' she uttered through her clenched teeth, her lashes lowered, wondering what he knew of her pain. She wished, as she put down the spoon in her barely touched dessert dish, that that reassuring hand hadn't come to rest across the back of her chair, enclosing Jarrad and her in their own private world. Wished that the others weren't talking quite so animatedly in a way that accentuated the intimacy between them. And, confident that they couldn't hear, for his ears only she breathed, 'It isn't every man who can entertain both his mistress and his wife at the same time—and without a glimmer of conscience!'

'Perhaps, darling, it's because, as you so often intimated in the past, I don't have one,' he suggested quietly, and though a smile touched his lips it did nothing to warm his eyes.

No, otherwise he couldn't have dismissed Ralph as mercilessly as he had, she thought, and the small gasp of anguish she struggled to contain changed to one of stifled shock as the barest touch of that arm against her shoulder brought her involuntarily closer to him.

'I don't see how you can accuse me of any undue attention towards Lauren tonight.'

Which was true, Kendal realised. Because if he was still harbouring feelings for his Sales Director then, surprisingly, he was keeping them remarkably concealed. In fact, Kendal had to admit that he had been more than attentive towards her tonight, treating her with a regard that was reminiscent of the old days. Even if it was, as she thought, because of how he knew she was suffering at the moment, slowly but surely it was beginning to eat away at her guarded circumspection, so that she was in danger of falling victim to his lethal magnetism, of becoming vulnerable as she had before—vulnerable and exposed.

But never again! she vowed, suddenly quipping, 'And am I supposed to get down on my knees to you for that?'

She tensed as hard fingers closed with subtle pressure on her arm.

'On your knees and begging for mercy after what you've put me through, Kendal Mitchell,' he whispered thickly, just a hair's breadth from her ear, so that to anyone else they would look engaged in a lovers' tête-à-tête.

After what she'd put him through!

Her eyes were heavy from the ache of his betrayal, her delicate face fraught from her scarred emotions.

'You don't know what—' she started to protest, but broke off as Paul suddenly sliced a question across the table.

'What do you think, Jarrad?' In the sudden break in the conversation everyone seemed to be waiting eagerly for his opinion. 'Lauren seems to think you're the only one capable of guiding her through the loopholes in that Bingham Agreement, and that with your help she'll be able to get them to close the deal.'

'She can do it,' he said succinctly, letting his arm drop casually from around Kendal's shoulders.

Bingham's, she knew, was another large customer who was being awkward about the terms TMS were proposing, a thing she had picked up from that phone call Jarrad had taken in the bedroom the other day.

'With old Ernest Bingham a woman-hater and a confessed male chauvinist at that! As far as he's concerned, business is a man's game, you know that. We could lose the whole deal…'

'Not with Lauren handling it.' Jarrad's confidence was unshakable.

'Thanks, darling.' Through glossy bronzed lips she blew him a more than grateful kiss across the table. 'It might still be a man's game in some areas, Paul,' she accepted with that unfaltering, self-assured smile, 'and not for your faint-hearted female. But this one's moved in a man's world long enough to know how to play by the rules.'

So typical of Lauren! Kendal thought. Still needing to prove her equal status. But the woman in Lauren hadn't failed to notice that intimate exchange between her, Kendal and Jarrad—to notice and resent it—which was why she had been prompted to slip in that dig about faint-hearted women. Women like herself, Kendal decided, surprisingly not intimidated by the other woman as she had been just a year ago.

The waiter came over then to consort with Jarrad, and at his suggestion they all moved into the large, yet cosy library to have their coffee.

Lauren had gone to fetch a file from her car, and, while the three men sat together to discuss business on the comfortable chairs on one side of the low oblong table, Virginia Forster joined Kendal on the velvet-covered sofa and seemed more than interested to hear about her work.

The questions were intended to help relieve her of her ordeal, she had the sensitivity to realise—help take her mind off things, if only for a while. She felt numb and dazed, though, as if she weren't really there at all. Therefore, she responded to the woman's kindness in a polite, yet mechanical fashion, wishing Diana Lawrence would come to her aid and chip in with something so that she wouldn't have to keep up the continual tedium of conversation. Sitting on her other side, however, the financial director's wife said next to nothing at all.

She was obviously a home-bird and clearly unused to finding herself in such awe-inspiring company, Kendal realised, feeling for her even through her own mental torment. The woman had scarcely spoken little more than the odd monosyllable all night.

Is that how I seemed when I was living with Jarred? she thought distractedly, seeing herself in Diana. So tongue-tied? So under-confident? Was it any wonder he had turned to Lauren?

Hurting more than she could have imagined, she excused herself to go to the powder room.

The evening was proving more of a strain even than she had anticipated, and as she crossed the deep, springy carpet, the powder room's wide mirror reflected the hollow circles under her eyes and the stretched, translucent skin across her cheekbones.

The door opened and someone else came in. Lauren, she recognised immediately in the mirror.

The other woman came across and placed her file down beside the basin with her neat, bronze evening bag. Ever the businesswoman—upwardly climbing, sure of herself.

'I didn't like to say anything in front of the others—and I'm sure I don't have to.' She wasn't looking at Kendal, only at the pink tissue she was taking from the box on the vanity unit, provided for the benefit of the hotel's patrons. 'But I'm sure you know I feel the same as everyone else does about Jarrad's little boy.'

'Thanks.' Kendal's voice was clipped. It wasn't easy to talk about. She noted though how Lauren had managed, effectively and probably deliberately, even in her commiserations, to omit Kendal from the equation.

'I must admit I was really surprised to see you here to-night. I'm sure everyone else was too,' she expressed, blotting her lips. 'Although I suppose it's a good thing if you can still come out and enjoy yourself.'

Kendal could only stare at the woman's cool, confident reflection, feeling her nails digging into her palms until she thought they would draw blood. How could Lauren even imagine...?

'I'm only here because Jarrad wanted me with him,' she said, wishing she could believe that entirely, her voice little more than a trembling croak.

Lauren cocked a glance at her through the mirror, looking a little surprised.

'I suppose you feel you've got to stick together.' Carefully she was reapplying bronze lipstick from an expensive-looking gold case. 'Jarrad hasn't said as much, but is that why you're back together?'

Kendal steeled herself before replying. 'What do you think?' she asked. She couldn't bring herself to inform the woman that she was only with Jarrad temporarily—only until...

The vision of a future in which she would know her present pain duplicated ten times over—a future not only without Jarrad, but without Matthew too—almost made her gasp with its intensity.

Her lashes came down as, like an automaton, she took her powder compact from her bag, trying not to let her fears run riot, trying not to think.

'I think you didn't care enough about him then—when you had the chance—and you're only with him now because you need him to support you through all this,' Lauren shook her by remarking, blotting her lipstick with the tissue.

'And I think that it really isn't any of your business, Lauren,' Kendal said bitterly. Oh, if only she could believe that! That her husband hadn't sought comfort in this woman's arms!

'Perhaps if you'd concentrated on being more of a wife to Jarrad instead of trying to compete with me all the time you might have made more of a success out of being a mother!' Lauren responded nastily. 'I'd never leave a man and then deny him rights to his own child!'

The weight of guilt in Kendal's chest was almost crushing, and it was all she could do not to let it reveal itself on an agonised sob.

'Is that what he told you?'

'He didn't have to.' Lauren dropped her lipstick back into her bag, snapped the clasp together. 'I've seen him in the office—I know what he's been through these past months, driving himself to the limit.'

'And I suppose that makes you an expert on my husband, does it?' Kendal breathed, unable to imagine the man she had known being as affected by anything as much as Lauren was trying to make her believe. 'And you wouldn't deny a man access to his child because you wouldn't have a child, would you, Lauren?' Kendal went on to point out to her in a voice that shook, well aware that the woman didn't like children, guessing that Lauren was speaking to her like this only because, surprisingly, Jarrad had been showing *her* so much attention all evening.

'It would tie you down too much. Keep you from continually having to prove you're as good as he is. Because that's what you're doing, isn't it?' Amazingly, from somewhere, her new maturity had brought her insight into the fact that it was insecurity that made Lauren continually strive to prove herself in the way she did. 'Isn't it?'

'Well, why not? It's true, isn't it? And Jarrad respects me for it. Why else would he leap in and back me up like he did this evening if he didn't respect and admire my capabilities? You couldn't even cope with being his wife— let alone help him run his empire! What else could you offer him except sex, housekeeping and a lot of fancy decorations? A man like Jarrad needs more than that to come home to at the end of a day!'

Lauren was grasping at straws, Kendal thought, because Jarrad would never have confided that to the other woman. But she could see suddenly how jealous of her Lauren was, when she had always thought it the other way around!

She wanted to bite out that Lauren could have him—that

he meant nothing to her! Only she couldn't because she wasn't sure that it was true.

Instead she said simply, 'As I said, our marriage is no-body's business but our own.' And turned and walked away.

She was still hurting from that little interlude with Lauren when Jarrad drove them home an hour or so later.

'You're quiet,' he remarked, after he had parked the car in the garage and was following her through the connecting door into the house. 'Did I demand too much of you—dragging you along with me tonight?' There was a surprising degree of solicitude in his voice.

The demand he had spoken of had stretched her nerves too far to be soothed by it, however, and as she came through the large fitted kitchen she threw tartly over her shoulder, 'You should have warned me that your girlfriend was going to be there, flaunting her assets for all and sundry to appreciate! If you had you couldn't even have whipped me into going with you!'

She was through the hall and halfway up the stairs before she realised he was following her.

'How the hell was I supposed to know she was going to be there?' he tossed after her, those deep tones harshened by impatience. 'It was as big a surprise to me as it was to you when she turned up!'

She knew he was telling the truth. Hadn't she heard what he'd said to Lauren? Nevertheless, the things the woman had said had bruised her too much emotionally to ration-alise even to herself, and woundedly she slung back, 'Oh, poor, innocent Jarrad!'

Her eyes, spitting green fire, clashed with the dark, rising fury in his. 'Yes, that's right, Kendal! As innocent as you are!'

What was that supposed to mean? Was he making some sort of reference to Tony?

'I fail to see what you're getting so steamed up about!' he rasped behind her before she could ask him.

'Well, what did you expect?' She swung round with a swish of blue silk at the top of the stairs. 'For obvious reasons she isn't exactly my favourite person!'

'And what are those reasons, Kendal?'

She didn't answer, but stormed down to her room.

'All invented and trumped up by a paranoid, over-imaginative little mind!'

'Paranoid?' She rounded on him as he strode after her into the master bedroom. 'It doesn't take much imagination for anyone with even half a mind to realise that she's madly in love with you!'

'Hah!' His laugh was harsh. 'Lauren's only interested in power.'

'And you've got plenty of that!' she accused, tossing her bag down on the dressing table. 'By the ton!'

'That isn't my problem.'

'No, it's clearly an advantage, seeing that it acts like an aphrodisiac on your closest colleague! What was it supposed to prove tonight, Jarrad? That you can resist her when you're in my company?'

'That I can resist the woman, full stop! Hasn't it ever occurred to you that all I ever wanted was you and Matthew?'

'Then why did you drive us away?'

He came round the bed, all lean power and brooding masculinity, as she took a floral cream kimono out of the wardrobe.

'I didn't. You did that yourself with your own petty jealousy and suspicion.'

'And lack of communication, I suppose!'

'Perhaps.'

'Yes, and all on my part!' she accused him, tossing the kimono down and sweeping determinedly past him. 'Perhaps I wasn't the perfect wife and mother for you either!

Perhaps if I'd been as clever as Lauren you'd have liked me better instead!'

'I told you. All I ever wanted in my life was you and Matthew.'

'But Matthew isn't here!' She screamed it at him, the weight of her guilt and torture coming crashing down around her so that she just wanted to hurt him—hurt herself—punish herself for all that she thought she deserved. 'That's all you succeeded in doing! Losing our son!'

'Kendal, stop it!'

She couldn't. The strain of the past week, combining with all she had had to endure from Lauren Westgate that evening, had stretched her beyond her limits.

'Why? Don't you want to hear the truth? Perhaps you'd like to be with her!'

'I said stop it!'

His face like thunder, he started back around the bed to where she was pulling off her neat silver earrings.

'Stay away from me!' She hurled one at him, but he ducked and it arrowed over his shoulder, hitting the radiator on the far wall with a clang.

'I said stay away from me!'

The other one followed, meeting exactly the same fate.

'No, Kendal. I think it's time you understood.'

'Understood what?' she said, backing away as he still kept coming. 'Do you imagine I'd ever believe anything you said?'

'Quite frankly, no.' His mouth turning grim, he suddenly reached for her as she backed into the hard wood of the chest of drawers. 'I don't think you'd trust a man if he came down out of the sky with a halo round his head! But how much more of this is it going to take before you'll realise? I'm *not* your father!'

So that was it! He was using the tragedy of her background to absolve himself from his own sins. Never mind about Matthew. Never mind that she was dying inside...!

'So it's my fault, is it? It's all my fault!' Hurting, hating him, she tried to wrench herself away from him, and, when she couldn't, panicking, unthinking, she turned her elbow hard into his solar plexus.

He caught his breath, doubling over, and she found her freedom. But only for an instant. In the next, hard fingers snapped around her arm, stalling her precipitate flight so that she bumped clumsily into the chest again, sending a brass candlestick crashing over as he swung her angrily to face him.

'You little...' She didn't even catch the word he stifled beneath his breath, fighting the hard strength of his hands now as he fought to restrain hers from making clawing contact with his face.

'Let me go! I hate you!'

'Yes!' he rasped, as though it were the ultimate acknowledgement he would ever make, and then his mouth came down, wiping the futile protest from her lips.

His arms tightening around her, he pulled her into the hard power of his body, his strength subduing the fight she was trying to put up against him. His hand plunged into her hair, grasping the fiery silk, dragging her head back so hard that it hurt. And, oh, God, she welcomed the pain, sinking her nails into the expensive cloth of his jacket, dragging them down his back, wanting to provoke his anger, incite him into hurting her so that she could forget this ravaging anguish in the punishing ferocity of his anger.

She heard his groan as his mouth found her throat, burning savage kisses on the smooth, pale column he had exposed. And then suddenly it wasn't anger any more. It was need. A fierce, raw emotion that had her straining toward him as his mouth found hers again, responding to his kiss with an urgency of her own—an urgency that disregarded the guilt and self-debasement she knew would follow her wanting this man who had wronged and humiliated her. Because only losing herself in this reckless passion for him could bring her the oblivion she craved.

'Oh, God...'

His voice was thick with wanting as he tore the impeding silk from her shoulders. She heard the delicate fabric give beneath the urgency of his hands, but she didn't care. His passion was almost brutal, and she was glorying in it, moving to slip her arms out of her jacket—to let him unfasten her zip—before first her skirt and then the silver camisole slid down her body. Then with deft but imperative fingers he undid the clasp of her bra.

His hands were rough against her breasts, but she didn't want it any other way. Tenderness would only have given her time to think and feel, and she wanted only to be driven by her physical senses, to be consumed by the fires that only he could ignite in her, in a conflagration of her most basic needs.

And a conflagration it was as he pulled her back into his arms. The sensuality of his clothes against her warm, yielding nakedness drew a small, shuddering gasp from her throat, heightening her arousal with the decadent excitement of being so singularly exposed to him.

Desperately her fingers tugged at his shirt, dragging it out of the narrow black band around his waist, trembling as they tried to unfasten the buttons without much success. Impatiently he pushed her hands away and did it for her, slipping his jacket and shirt off in one smooth movement, tossing them down before picking her up and carrying her over to the bed.

His warm flesh against hers was more arousing than memory had prepared her for, and wildly her hands explored the smooth velvet of his shoulders, shaping the hard bulge of muscle beneath the crisp coarseness of his body hair until he came down beside her and claimed one breast with the suckling urgency of his mouth.

She was lost then to everything but the fire of need and desire and longing that was raging uncontrollably inside her, sweeping aside everything but the knowledge that almost without her being aware of it he had removed the last of his clothes.

She writhed desperately beneath him, like some unbroken animal fighting the bonds of a dominating master, crazy for the ecstasies of release.

He took her then, without any restraint, plunging into the moist warmth of her body.

She gave a small cry, and sank her nails into the hard sinews of his back, rising to meet his rhythm, the fierceness of each thrust obliterating the agonies of the past week and driving the last thoughts from her mind until there was nothing but one man and one woman, and the boundless, blinding reaches of the universe.

She awoke while it was still dark, hot beneath the duvet with which he must have covered her as she slept, spent after their frenzied passion.

She felt bruised and tender, and grew hotter as she remembered how she had invited—no, incited—the violence of his lovemaking. The shame of it made her cheeks burn, and her body throbbed as it acknowledged the naked length of him still lying there beside her. She could hear the slow, steady rhythm of his breathing.

A shaft of light fell across his face from a brilliant moon, and she turned to study his profile, her breath catching in her lungs.

In sleep he looked so like Matthew, the wide mouth relaxed, that dark hair uncustomarily tousled. She wanted to reach out and touch that strong cheek, run her finger down the length of that uncompromising jaw made vulnerable by sleep. But the contact that had been so essential and inevitable when she had been driven by the force of her passion now seemed thoroughly taboo.

He had made love to her because he hadn't been able to stop himself, caught—just as she had been—in the snare of their mutual desire. Nothing had changed. Not Lauren. Whatever he said, the fact that he had cheated on her with the other woman wouldn't go away, even if, as he had professed tonight, he didn't want her now. Nothing could alter that, or the way he had driven a wedge between Ralph and Chrissie.

Tears filled her eyes and she turned onto her back, staring through the darkness at the ceiling.

Why had it been her fate to fall in love with him? she agonised. And, thinking of Chrissie—where the hell was she? Why couldn't she pick up a phone and ring, just to let her know that she was all right? True, it was early days yet, and she knew her sister would probably contact her eventually. But she needed to hear from her—and never so much as now, while she was going through this torture over Matthew! It was silly, she knew, but she was afraid. She just didn't like the feeling that her sister, as well as her baby, had disappeared off the face of the earth.

She sat up with a start, suddenly wide awake—alert. There was something… Something that had been niggling at her all day.

It was that card at Chrissie's. That postcard she had almost started to read before realising that it wasn't addressed to *her*. It had been signed by Ralph. That much she had digested. But what was Ralph doing writing to Chrissie, when Chrissie was supposed to be with him?

Only now did the significance of that card intrude enough upon her thoughts for her to wonder why she hadn't considered it before. But then she was so traumatised at the moment because of Matthew that half the time she didn't know whether she was coming or going, or even what she was doing—let alone being conscious of anything anyone else was doing! But supposing Chrissie hadn't…

She couldn't even shape the thought that was forming in her brain. What was she thinking? Imagining?

As if a plug had suddenly been pulled, draining her of all her strength, she lay back limply against the pillow.

Beside her she heard Jarrad stir in his sleep. He turned onto his side, facing her, his arm coming heavily and possessively across her breasts.

Chrissie was somewhere in Europe, she thought, above

a mounting awareness of that warm, male body next to hers. She had telephoned from the airport the day she'd left. In which case why had that card from—where was it? Italy?—been signed by Ralph? Unless, of course, he had posted it over two weeks ago, before he'd invited Chrissie to join him, and it had taken all this time for it to reach her. That wasn't unheard of...

Lying there in the darkness, listening to Jarrad's deep, regular breathing, she deduced that that had to be the answer.

Nevertheless, even through the faint stirring of desire from the weight of that strong arm across her breasts, something still continued to nag at her. She had to know for sure...

Eventually, deciding that she was never going to get back to sleep, very carefully she lifted the heavy arm from around her slender body and slipped quietly out of bed.

CHAPTER SIX

THE light Kendal had left on in Chrissie's bedroom the previous day was the only one burning in any of the houses when she turned into the street and pulled up outside the one where her sister lived.

A chorus of waking birds sang out piercingly on the air, and the pale light of dawn stole into the hallway as she opened Chrissie's front door and closed it again, snapping on the light.

The postcard was still sticking out of the letter rack where she had left it on the telephone table.

Well, of course it was, she thought. Was else had she been imagining?

Her fingers, though, were trembling as she drew it out from the rack. And this time, after only a cursory glance at the glorious Italian panorama, she flipped it over, purposefully reading every line Ralph had written.

See what you missed? By walking out on me last Thursday and deciding to go home as you did. Perhaps I was entirely selfish, as you said, Chrissie; I don't know. I only know that all I want is to be with you, and that for what it's worth I'm sorry, darling. Maybe some time in the future we can try again.
Yours ever, Ralph.

So they had had another one of their rows and Chrissie had walked out. Flown home. But where was she? Kendal couldn't make it out.

The card referred to Thursday. It wasn't dated, and she couldn't read the postmark, but she knew it could only have been the Thursday of the previous week.. Therefore where was Chrissie if she wasn't with Ralph?

Horrors gripped her as she remembered the state her younger sister had been in the last time she and her husband had separated. But at that time she had been on the phone to Kendal day and night. And if she had come back she couldn't have failed to have heard about the nightmare her sister and her husband were going through. And, if nothing else, surely that would have been enough to shock her out of any depression she might have been suffering? To force her to forget her own problems. So why hadn't she telephoned? Been in touch?

With her head swimming now, Kendal considered the possibility that Chrissie might have stayed on in Italy on her own, then dismissed it as unlikely. It wasn't the sort of thing her sister would do. So what had happened to her? Where was she if she'd walked out on Ralph a week ago— last Thursday? Thursday—only the day before Matthew...

She slammed the lid on her fears that something might have happened to her sister as well as to her baby, her thoughts whirling as all the events of the week coalesced in a melting pot of confused anguish.

A ransom, the police had suspected was the reason for his kidnap initially. But then they had said that perhaps he'd been taken by someone...

An icy chill spread through her. Dear God! What was she talking herself into believing?

'*No!*' The cry escaped her as she tossed down the card and almost without thinking ran upstairs. All right, Chrissie *was* desperate for a child. And, true, she'd already suffered two miscarriages before her last pregnancy, which had made losing that baby so much more traumatic. But Chrissie loved Matthew. Why was Kendal even supposing she'd take him?

Another small sob escaped her. She was becoming paranoid. Jarrad had been right about that. For what other reason would she be imagining her sister was the kidnapper? A child abductor? It didn't make sense!

From somewhere she found the presence of mind to look in Chrissie's wardrobe. Her suitcase wasn't there. How could it be, Kendal reasoned, when her sister was very probably still in Italy? When she hadn't come back, as Ralph had supposed, but was probably taking a well-earned holiday, trying to pick up the pieces of her life after another painful break-up with her husband?

But you know you left that light on before.

Even as she strove to earnestly convince herself of what must have happened, other doubts surfaced to torment her. Because it was true. She looked up at the illuminated pink shade as though it were a traitor that had just betrayed her to the worst possible enemy.

She knew she had left it on during a previous visit, some time during that week before Matthew had been snatched. And yet yesterday, when she had come upstairs, she had been ready to accept that she must have forgotten to do so—had even rebuked herself for doing it. But she *had* switched it on. She remembered now, despite everything—in spite of all that had happened since. She had made a point of double-checking, had been conscientious in making sure that her sister's property was safe.

'No. It can't be!' It was a small, choked whisper, and she dropped down onto the double bed which, in happier times, her sister had shared with Ralph. So Chrissie *must* have come back. But where was she? And Matthew? Oh, God, where was Matthew?

Paralysed by a numbing immobility, she started as the telephone beside the bed suddenly burred through the silence. She stared at it for a few moments, letting it ring.

Perhaps it was Chrissie!

She snatched it up, not sparing any logic for the question of why Chrissie would be ringing her own number, her knuckles white with tension as she gripped the receiver, waiting, breath held, for the caller to speak.

'Chrissie?' It was like a mocking echo of her own thoughts. *'Chrissie?'* Again that hesitant, slightly puzzled voice. A voice Kendal would have known anywhere. Jarrad's! 'Chrissie? Are you there?'

Kendal stared into the mouthpiece, her fine brows drawn together. Why was Jarrad ringing her sister—and at this time of the morning—when he knew as well as Kendal did that Chrissie was away?

'Chrissie?' Again there was some hesitation, as though for some reason he suspected the person he was ringing might not want to answer. 'It's Jarrad. I need to talk to you. About Kendal. Kendal...and Matthew.'

Kendal's face twisted into an agony of bewilderment.

'Chrissie?' There was more of a compelling demand in the deep voice now.

Hardly knowing what she was doing, Kendal dropped the phone with a resounding little clatter onto its rest. She couldn't talk to him! She couldn't talk to anyone! Nothing was making sense. She felt as if she was going mad!

Jarrad wanted to talk to Chrissie—about *her*. Her and Matthew! But why? What did he want to talk to Chrissie about that could possibly concern Matthew? What was he doing ringing here at all?

She jumped as the phone suddenly started its unfamiliar burr for a second time, and after four or five rings she picked it up.

'Chrissie?' Jarrad's voice sounded more urgent this time.

'It isn't Chrissie. It's Kendal,' she murmured in a weak, desolate voice.

'Kendal?' Shock ran with hard puzzlement through the deep tones.

'What the hell are you doing there? At this hour? I woke up and you were gone. I've been at my wits' end wondering where you were!'

Had he?

'Oh, Jarrad! It's Chrissie...I think she's got Matthew!' The words tumbled out before she could stop them.

There was a momentary silence at the other end of the phone. 'What—makes you say that?' he enquired hesitantly.

'I just know it! There's a card from Ralph here. She left Italy over a week ago! She came back here. I know! Oh, Jarrad…!'

'Stay where you are. I'm coming over.'

He was calm—remarkably so. In control as always. And Kendal welcomed that leadership quality of his as she went back downstairs to wait for him, trying to reason, trying to think.

If her sister had taken Matthew, where would she have taken him? And why would she have taken him? she wondered, pacing the lounge, bathed now by the glittering gold of a new day.

Chrissie wanted a baby more than anything. But to steal someone else's? Her own nephew?

Tears bit behind Kendal's eyes as she thought how fond of him Chrissie was. Sometimes she'd thought it was only Matthew who had kept her sister going after that last miscarriage and her break-up with Ralph, both brought about directly as a result of Jarrad's pitiless actions.

But what state of mind must she be in for her to do a thing like this? Kendal worried, appalled. If she *had* done it. And then suddenly she thought it odd how Jarrad hadn't sounded surprised.

Distractedly she recalled his reaction when she had told him about Chrissie, suddenly waking up to the way he had responded—the fact that he hadn't told her she was being ridiculous. He'd sounded cagey—not shocked—when he'd asked her why she suspected her sister. Yes, that was it—cagey, she cogitated, as though he'd half expected it. As though he'd known…

Something cold and insidious started to trickle through her, heightening her confusion as she recalled the words he had breathed to her through the heat of his passion last night, before they had drifted off to sleep.

'I would do anything to keep you here. Here in my bed. In my life. You know that, don't you?'

Anything, her mind echoed as she dropped down onto the settee. But did that anything include…?

She cupped her hands over her nose and mouth, finding it an effort to breathe. Don't be ridiculous! she berated herself again. Whatever else he's done, he's no kidnapper! And he's as cut up by Matthew's disappearance as you are.

Wasn't everything he said—every gesture—evidence of that?

But men were brilliant actors. The warning her mother had issued to her all those years ago rose from the dark recesses of her mind to taunt her—a warning never to wholly believe a man, never to trust.

Well, hadn't she been right? As she tried to shake the thoughts away, that torturing little voice kept relentlessly on. *He cheated on you, didn't he? And, anyway, how did he know that Chrissie might be home?*

She took a few deep, steadying breaths into her palms. She was going insane! She had to be! He'd never have been that desperate—that determined—to get her back into his life again…would he? She gave a violent shudder at the damning realisation of her own thoughts. Involving the police? Involving her sister? Hurting her that much?

Of course he wouldn't! she assured herself with a hard derision at the way her mind was working. What was she imagining? That he was in some sort of conspiracy with Chrissie to stop her taking Matthew out of the country? To force her to go back with him by arranging to have Matthew taken away? Because if she believed an absurdity like that what interpretation would she put on his ringing here this morning? That having made love to her—got her back in his bed, in his life—he'd finally decided to call a halt to his cruel machinations?

Oh, dear God! Whatever was she letting herself believe?

She didn't know how long she sat there, staring at the patterned weave of Chrissie's wicker coffee-table, but it seemed no time at all before she heard the low growl of the Porsche as it turned into the road, then pulled up outside the house.

The bell sounded ominously in the hall.

He was standing there in a cream polo shirt and light trousers, his hair tousled as though he had done nothing more than rake his fingers through it after getting out of bed, and his face was set in grim lines as he strode in.

'What is it?' he asked in a surprisingly gentle voice as he saw her backing away. 'What's wrong?'

Shouldn't he have known? Should he have had any right to ask?

'You knew,' she whispered, her face pale and tortured. 'You *knew*.'

'Knew?' He was looking at her askance as he came away from the front door he had pushed closed, frowning down at her in her lacy cotton top and jeans. 'Knew what?'

'About Chrissie.'

He shrugged. 'I think *guessed* would be more appropriate. And not until—' He broke off, reading the pained accusation in her eyes, accusation that had turned to puzzlement even before he said, 'My God! Kendal? What the hell are you implying?'

She stepped back from his threatening stance, coming up against the wall at the foot of the stairs.

'But you rang here. You wanted to talk to her.' She couldn't get anything straight in her mind—his guilt. His innocence. Chrissie's. What did it matter? Matthew was still missing! 'I thought you—'

'You thought *what*?'

His fingers on her upper arms were bruising in their angry demand.

'I don't know. I—' She put her hand to her forehead. 'Oh, goodness, Jarrad! What was I supposed to think? You rang up and asked to speak to Chrissie. You said you wanted to talk to her about Matthew...' He had, hadn't he?

She hadn't dreamt it? 'What made you think she was here? Unless you...'

'Unless I what? Arranged his kidnapping myself—and with your own sister?'

Well, wasn't that what she had talked herself into half believing?

'You really hate me, don't you?' he breathed, and thrust her away from him as though he couldn't bear to touch her, so hard she almost toppled back over the bottom stair. 'Whatever last night was supposed to tell me, you were certainly right about that!'

No, I wasn't! she wanted to cry out, wishing he hadn't reminded her about last night, about her foolhardy, reckless surrender to him. But no matter how hard she had tried to hate him over the past year she couldn't. Fool that she was, she couldn't!

'You're warped, Kendal,' he tossed at her roughly. 'It isn't only Chrissie who's got problems—it's you as well! Do you really think I'd be that mercenary—or even that stupid?' Deep grooves etched his face. 'Whatever happened to trust? Or doesn't that even come into the equation?'

'How can it?' she sobbed. 'When I don't know anything any more!'

'You mean you don't know me.' His tone was tough, implacable.

'I know what you're capable of,' she whispered with trembling poignancy.

'Do you?' His tone was harsh, but there was a stark bleakness to his features that made her heart lurch with an emotion she didn't want to feel for him, an emotion that turned to raw pain when she saw the heat of disgust suddenly burning in his eyes.

'Well, put yourself in my place!' she cried plaintively in defence. 'What *am* I supposed to think? Feel? Can you imagine how it feels discovering that the person closest to you in the world is probably responsible for bringing you the most pain you're ever going to have to endure?'

'No, I can't begin to imagine what that's like,' he emphasised in a purely sarcastic tone, and, when she ignored him, 'I take it by that you mean Chrissie?' Obviously he hadn't flattered himself that he was the one closest to her. Or perhaps he imagined he wasn't guilty of ever causing her any pain.

'Yes, Chrissie! My own sister as you so clearly pointed out! I just don't believe she'd do it!'

'Not without any help from the big bad ogre, your child's father? Isn't that what you're intimating? Well, I'm sorry, Kendal, but I think you're going to have to face the facts,' he went on roughly, giving her no quarter. 'Your precious Chrissie can, and probably has, all by herself! She's crazy for a child—as I'd have thought you'd know.'

'Yes, but—' She ignored that last, oddly castigating note in his voice and followed him into the lounge. 'How did you know? You haven't been in touch with her since we split up, have you? You said you'd guessed that it was her. How could you?' She looked mystified, her eyes half-accusing, as he turned round.

'What are you imagining?' There was a humourless curl to his lower lip. 'That I've been in contact with Chrissie over the past six months since you disappeared? Trying to reach you through her?' He gave a self-denigrating little grimace. 'Oh, I thought about it! But sorry, Kendal, I left that little stone completely unturned.'

'Then how do you know how desperately she wants a family? Or are you just guessing after the one you deprived her of?'

Clearly she had hit a raw nerve, and she saw that masculine mouth compress into a harsh, thin line. 'I've told you before. I didn't know she was pregnant.'

Kendal's chin came up as she looked him squarely in the eyes. 'Would you have cared?' she enquired of him bitterly.

'What do you think?' He lifted a hand to silence anything she might be going to say. 'No, don't answer that. I know.'

'So what made you guess that it might be her? And why did you think you could contact her here—at this hour of the morning?'

One thick black eyebrow arched severely. 'I might be inclined to ask you a similar question. What drove you to getting up and driving over here before it was barely light?'

Kendal frowned. She had to think about it now. 'I think it was that card…' She gave a jerk of her head towards the hall, wondering what she had done with the postcard she'd been reading before she had dashed upstairs to look for Chrissie's case. 'It was there with the rest of the post I picked up yesterday. It was from Ralph.'

'Exactly. Ralph.'

The line between Kendal's brows deepened.

'There was a message from him—on the answer machine,' he started to explain. 'He must have phoned when we were out yesterday evening, although when we got back last night checking for messages was the last thing on my mind.'

Kendal felt hot colour stain her cheeks and couldn't look at him, remembering how desperately she had given herself to him, welcomed the fierceness of his driving passion.

'Something woke me. I'm not sure what it was. Probably the fact that I was alone,' he was surmising, half to himself. 'I looked all over the house for you. That was when I noticed the answer machine flashing in the study. He'd been trying to ring Chrissie for days, but couldn't reach her, and, not knowing where you were living, in desperation he rang me.'

Desperation, Kendal decided, because it would have been a last resort for Ralph to phone the man who had destroyed his career with TMS, killed his unborn child and wrecked his marriage.

'He's still in Italy, and he sounded at the end of his tether on the tape, so I returned his call this morning. Or, rather, *earlier* this morning.' He grimaced, squinting towards the window where the half-risen sun was now dazzling between the houses on the opposite side of the road. 'I was going to leave it at first until a more respectable hour, but something made me feel that it couldn't wait.

'Ralph was worried about where Chrissie was. I said I'd thought she was with him. But he said they'd had a row and she'd left—come home early. When I told him we hadn't seen her, he started telling me things. Things I thought surely you'd know.'

'What sort of things?' Kendal subsided onto the settee.

'Like why he and Chrissie broke up.'

'Well, we all know that, don't we?' she returned caustically, and saw the way that Jarrad's mouth thinned.

'You still think it was my fault? That I drove him to drink, and subsequently to near financial ruin?'

'Didn't you?' Kendal accused him. 'You and Lauren both! You concocted a plan and between you you managed to get rid of him. You can't honestly deny that!'

'Yes, we got rid of him—as you put it—but it was only in the interest of the company that he was asked to leave, whatever else you might like to think. He'd started drinking—oh, not that much, but certainly more than was wise— long before we'd decided it couldn't go on. It wasn't losing his job that drove him into that downward spiral of irresponsibility. It was his marriage that did that.'

'What do you mean?' Kendal demanded, wondering how he could say that. Until Ralph and Chrissie's financial difficulties—brought about by the cruel way her brother-in-law had been sliced out of Jarrad's company—she had always imagined that their marriage had been a happy one. 'They were happy,' she emphasised aloud.

'Were they?' The grim lines of Jarrad's mouth assured her that he clearly presumed otherwise. 'So we were all led to believe. He was too embarrassed and ashamed of his marital problems to tell anyone; he told me so on the phone this morning. And it was Chrissie's neurosis that caused the split—that Ralph found he couldn't handle—her disillusionment over not being able to have a baby!'

Kendal was shaking her head, refusing to believe it. She'd always known how much Chrissie wanted a family—how unhappy she had been after each of those miscarriages, particularly the last one. But that it had led to the break-up of her marriage...

'You're making it up,' she breathed. Otherwise why hadn't Chrissie ever said anything to her? 'Just to justify your reasons for sacking him—because their marriage couldn't stand the strain!'

'Am I?' He came across and stood there, relentlessly unyielding, above her. 'You can't honestly say that your sister's always been an unshakable pillar of stability.'

'Because of that overdose she took?' Because he had known about that—known, and been indirectly responsible for it. And she knew now that he was right—and not just regarding that one incident. But she couldn't let him get away with trying to convince himself—and her—that he had had no hand in her sister's problems. 'It was a cry for help, and you know it! Any woman might have reacted in the same way after all she had been through—losing her third baby and then her husband walking out! It's hardly surprising she was driven to that after all you'd done!'

That wide chest rose and then fell again as he exhaled a long breath.

'I see. So I'm being blamed for that too, am I?' he uttered tonelessly. 'Well, believe what you like,' he went on, his voice harsher now. 'According to Ralph, the problems didn't really start until after you got pregnant.'

She looked at him, startled. 'After *I* got pregnant?' She couldn't take in what he was saying. It had been a period of her life that had been so happy—perhaps her happiest, she reflected painfully, although she had felt guilty, conceiving so easily when Chrissie had already had two miscarriages. But she'd thought her sister had been happy for her too. And now...

She felt an ache in her chest like a ton weight pressing against it. What had Chrissie really been feeling? Jealousy?

Resentment? An agonised little sound escaped her. Had she herself been so totally oblivious to how her sister had felt?

'And if you're in any doubt as to why we shouldn't begin looking for her—' Jarrad's voice cut in across her thoughts, steel-hard and uncompromising '—do you know why Chrissie walked out on Ralph last week? What the latest disagreement was all about?'

The eyes Kendal lifted to his were full of tortured appeal to him to protect her from the knowledge, because she knew that, whatever it was, it was going to hurt.

'It was over Ralph's refusal to adopt if Chrissie continues to find it impossible to carry a baby to its full term,' he stated nonetheless. 'That was when I told him what had happened to Matthew. And if it isn't one hell of a coincidence that she arrives home under those conditions the day before my boy goes missing...'

'We don't know that,' Kendal uttered, cut by that deliberately possessive pronoun he had used with regard to Matthew—as well as beginning to feel to blame somehow for her sister's behaviour which, with the relentless guilt she still carried that maybe she hadn't taken enough care of her son, was almost too much to cope with. After all, hadn't she been responsible for Chrissie's upbringing too?

'We don't know that she arrived home, do we?' she expanded wretchedly, aching for Matthew; aching as much to feel his father's arms around her, holding her, blotting out this pain as he had done for such a short, merciful time last night. 'Not for sure.'

'Don't we?' he said in a way that didn't need to be answered. And she thought, Of course. There was that light up there in the bedroom.

'Ralph said he saw her off,' Jarrad went on to elucidate. 'She didn't want him to, but he insisted. So unless the plane was hijacked, or disappeared over France somewhere, she arrived back here some time during that Thursday—no more than a matter of hours before Matthew went missing.'

And that would explain why he hadn't made a sound

when he'd been taken—because he would have recognised his aunt, been happy to see her, Kendal understood suddenly, her breath catching in an agony of loss that seemed to rip into her with savage talons as she pictured him toddling up to that gate on his unsteady little legs. Pictured his trusting baby face smiling up at Chrissie.

'What do we do now?' she murmured, staring through a numbing desolation at the casual, very masculine shoes planted firmly in front of her.

'Find her.' That grim determination in Jarrad's voice made her look up.

'And what will you do when you have?' Anguish lined her forehead. 'Destroy her as you destroyed Ralph?'

The harshening austerity of his features made her shudder. 'I'll do what I have to,' he said.

Which meant what? Bringing charges? She couldn't bear the thought of Chrissie going to prison. Seeing her sister annihilated by him at a time when she was obviously emotionally unstable.

'Supposing we can't? Find her, I mean,' she said, worried, plagued by the sudden fear that even if Matthew was with his aunt—and, in all probability, totally safe—there still remained the slimmest chance that they might not be found.

'We'll find her,' Jarrad said with hard assurance, looking as though he meant to start looking at that very moment while all she could do was sit there feeling totally helpless.

He was glancing round the room, looking for any clue, picking up a magazine that was sticking out of the rack on which something was scribbled, tossing it down on the cushion beside Kendal when he realised it wasn't anything relevant.

'Have you any idea where she might have gone?' Now he grabbed a notepad that had been lying on a chair beside a magnificent rubber plant.

'No.'

'She's your sister, for heaven's sake!' The glance he shot

her was demanding, exasperated. He flipped over a few pages of the notepad, scanning its contents, tossing that down too, as he had the magazine, when it failed to provide any clues. 'You must have some idea of where she might have taken him.'

'I haven't!' She sat there, shaking her head, her expression tortured.

'Think, damn you! Think!' He was on his haunches in front of her, his hard hands grasping her shoulders, face contorted with frustration and anger. Anger towards her, she realised—because, of course, she had doubted him, hadn't she? 'She's *your* sister, dammit! Aren't sisters supposed to know everything about each other?'

But they didn't, did they? she thought tormentedly. She'd thought she had known Chrissie, and look what had happened!

'Stop it!' she sobbed, because he was shaking her. 'I want to find him as much as you do, but I don't know! I just don't know!'

She had collapsed against him and, as if he had guessed at the limitations of her strength, his arms came around her.

'Oh, Jarrad.' She was sobbing into the warm column of his throat, wondering what this reckless emotion was that assured her she could bear anything just as long as he was there to hold her, when at the same time he was her enemy, threatening her happiness, her very existence, the essence of everything she treasured and held dear.

'Ralph seemed to indicate that she might have gone to Scotland.' There was a hoarseness in Jarrad's deep voice and his breath seemed to tremble through him as it stirred the soft red tendrils of hair at the side of Kendal's face.

'Scotland?' Against every longing in her body, she forced herself to withdraw a little so that she could look at him. Her eyes were puzzled, searching. *'Scotland?'* God! Why did his personal scent make her ache for him even in the depths of her trauma? 'Why on earth would he think that?'

'I don't know.' His voice was emotionless now. 'You tell me. I think he said something about Chrissie saying she wanted to live there. Finding some dream valley... I don't know. I might have got the wrong idea. He said so much I probably wasn't taking everything in...'

'Some dream valley?' Kendal sat back on the settee, racking her brains, trying to think back. Her dream valley...

'It was in the Lake District!'

'What was?' Jarrad was on his feet now.

'That's where it was. Above Borrowdale!'

'What are you talking about? For heaven's sake, Kendal!' Roughly he was hauling her to her feet. 'You aren't making sense!'

'The dream valley! She came to see me once when I was living in Scotland.' She barely noticed the pressure of those hard fingers on her arm. 'We took a trip down to the lakes—the northern lakes—and she fell instantly in love with Derwent Water. We got talking to one of the locals who let a holiday cottage there during the summer, and he said we could have the use of it...any time... What are you doing?'

He was pulling her after him towards the front door.

'I would have thought that was obvious,' he said, snapping off the hall light before urging her out into the early morning sunshine and the still deserted street.

Yes, it was. Totally obvious now. He had to be thinking exactly the same as she was. That, apart from being one of the loveliest valleys in England, Borrowdale was perhaps also one of the remotest. Ideal for someone seeking solitude, relaxation, or simply an escape.

'Oh, Jarrad. What are you going to do?' Beneath the overwhelming longing to see Matthew again, and her own anger at her sister, she was nursing the dread that he might make Chrissie pay—and over the odds—for even daring to imagine that she could take Matthew from him and get away with it. He'd always liked Chrissie, had got on well with her, but that had been before Ralph caught him in that compromising position with Lauren, and Kendal knew from the experience of that little episode how ruthless he could be.

'I wouldn't worry about your sister if I were you,' he advised as he unlocked the Porsche he had parked behind her own small saloon, and opened the passenger door for her to step in. 'She's going to get all the attention she needs. I suggest you use this journey to worry about your own future because when we find Matthew—after all this—I never intend letting him out of my sight for a single day!

'And if you're wondering about the ramifications of that, then I'll tell you, you've got every need to because it means exactly what it sounds like. He's living with me—in my house—under my roof—where I can keep a permanent eye on him. And if you've got any regard for the stability of our child's future then you'll pack in that glorious career of yours, forget what differences there are between us and try to make it work for his sake! Those are the terms. You can take them or leave them—personally, I don't care!'

And that was that, she thought, feeling the dark clutches of her destiny closing around her with the slamming of the car door, because it wasn't only Jarrad's hard resolve that was going to determine she do exactly as he said, for the time being at any rate. Fear, remorse and guilt—perhaps guilt most of all—had already driven her to decide that, when Matthew was back safely in her arms, after the torturous worry and anguish of the past week, she would never be able to bear being parted from him ever again.

And if giving him total security meant not working, always being there, even allowing him to live with both parents, then so be it. She didn't care any more what happened to her, or how she felt, or how badly bruised her emotions had been by her husband's infidelity with Lauren. She would close them off, as she had learned to do before, because it was Matthew who had to come first, and for whom she would do anything—even if that meant going back with Jarrad.

CHAPTER SEVEN

THE cottage stood on a remote hillside, a good mile or so from any other dwelling.

'A cosy little nook', was how its owner's son-in-law had described it when they had traced him by a process of elimination through various sources in the village, and it was.

Nestling under a ridge, halfway up the craggy hillside, the whitewashed stone of the house gave onto a wild, walled garden that fell away with the stony track to the narrow road and the verdant slopes, reaching down to the breathtaking splendour of the valley: emerald fields, criss-crossed by hedges and low stone walls, quaint cottages and a bridge that spanned the stream, reflecting like a silver ribbon in the sun.

Kendal, however, was too keyed up to enjoy the view or, indeed, to take in anything of her surroundings.

Her heart was beating weakeningly fast as Jarrad came around and helped her out of the car, which he had parked a little way down the track so as not to immediately alarm or raise suspicion with anyone who might be in the cottage.

Automatically he took her hand, the action having the power to stir her even at a time like this. But she hardly dared breathe as together they walked up the hill, keeping within the screen of trees and bushes running alongside the track obscuring them from the house, because they weren't even sure—from the man's description of the woman to whom he said his father-in-law had let the property—if it was Chrissie. She certainly hadn't given Chrissie Langdon as her name. His father-in-law, he had said, was on a fishing holiday in Scotland, and so he was unable to get the exact details. But did she have a baby? He didn't think so. No, he was almost certain his father-in-law had let it to a woman on her own.

A fan of dark foliage brushed Kendal's face, its cool dampness from the light shower they had had on the drive up here making her shiver.

Swiftly Jarrad held it back for her to pass, his bare forearm as it touched her cheek oddly impersonal, yet so gentle that a quiver of emotion ran through her.

'Supposing it isn't her?'

Her eyes were like wide green pools in the harrowed framework of her face.

'Let's not suppose anything yet,' he advised phlegmatically, although he had to be feeling equally as fraught as she was.

No, of course they shouldn't, she thought, because there was also the worst possibility that she hardly dared contemplate—that it *was* Chrissie, but that she would be alone. Because who was to say that her younger sister, tormented by these latest problems in her marriage, might not simply just have wanted time to herself after coming back from the Continent, simply to be on her own? The house was an ideal retreat, and cutting herself off from the outside world could have kept her entirely ignorant of the awful thing that had happened to her nephew. But that would only mean something more terrible than they feared already—that Matthew had been taken by a total stranger, with all the frightening connotations such an idea presented, and that they were nowhere nearer finding him than they had been six hours ago.

She had to stifle a surge of rising panic—the cry that she could so easily have let escape from her throat. It wouldn't do any good to fall to pieces now.

'Do you want me to do this alone?'

He had guessed, of course, how she was feeling—because wasn't he sharing all the same fears and suspicions too? But she shook her head, not trusting herself to speak.

Her throat felt raw with tension as they came into full view of the house. To one side was a small outbuilding that had obviously been converted to a garage, although its wooden doors were padlocked and didn't offer any clues as to whether it housed a vehicle—Chrissie's or anybody else's.

She felt Jarrad's arm go around her as they came down the path to the front porch. There was a clothesline, she noticed, around the other side of the house, with a few items of washing hanging on it—towels, a sheet, an unfamiliar skirt—nothing that pointed immediately to the occupation of a child, or even to Chrissie.

Still with his arm around her, Jarrad tapped almost tentatively on the door.

There was no reply. He rapped again, harder this time, his dark head bowed, listening for any movement inside the house. Kendal stood stock-still, her breath seeming as though it was trapped inside her.

She felt the loss of Jarrad's arm as he stepped back to glance up at the tiny windows above them, then moved forward to knock again just as the door opened a crack.

A slim, cautious-looking figure peered through it.

Chrissie! Kendal recognised her a second before Jarrad spoke her sister's name.

Realising who it was, quickly Chrissie tried to shut the door, but with one swift movement Jarrad had lodged his foot in the gap, and Chrissie gave a cry as sheer brute strength overcame her futile attempts to keep him out.

'No! You can't come in here!' She made a grab for him as he did just that, but that strong arm shook off her desperate, ineffectual grasp.

'Why not, Chrissie? Have you anything to hide?'

Her sister looked drawn, pale—Kendal would recall only being vaguely aware of thinking that afterwards—her enormous brown eyes alarmed in the small oval of her face. But at that moment, rushing in behind Jarrad, Kendal's mind was only on finding Matthew.

'No! No, you can't go in there!' Chrissie protested, because he had brushed past her through to the tiny living room although Kendal was ahead of him now, a small sound bringing her through into another cosy room at the back.

For one fleeting moment, she stood, transfixed by the sight of the little boy who was sitting there on the carpet, gurgling to himself as he played happily with some coloured bricks.

'Matthew!'

There would be no recollection, later, of running across the room, of scooping him up into her arms with all the fierce instincts of protection that only a mother could possess. But somehow he was crushed against her breast, and she was holding him as though she would never let him go, cradling his tiny head while her other arm curled protectively under his bottom.

He had made some surprised sound when she had picked him up, some small note of protest at the fierceness of her embrace, although that didn't matter. Because what mattered was that he was safe and well and overjoyed to see her, and that she heard that one sound she had prayed for and yet had dreaded she might never hear again, that innocently heart-wrenching, 'Mummy!'.

With her cheek against his temple, she sobbed into his hair, and it was like that that Jarrad saw her as he burst into the room.

She didn't even catch his whispered, 'Matthew!' And when he asked her, 'Is he...all right?' she could only nod, her tear-filled eyes and trembling smile saying it all.

'Oh, please...please don't be angry!' Chrissie was there right behind him, grabbing his arm again, halting his progress across the room. 'I didn't mean any harm! I only wanted him to have a home! Oh, Jarrad, please! Please don't be angry!'

Through her own sobs and Matthew's little protests at being clasped so tightly, Kendal could only gaze helplessly at her younger sister.

Chrissie was clutching Jarrad's shoulders, sobbing so desperately that suddenly her small, thin body seemed to crumple, her hands clawing down over his waist and lean hips, down the length of his long legs, her fingers twisting in the fine, quality cloth of his trousers as she collapsed in an undignified heap at his feet.

'I didn't mean him any harm! Really I didn't!'

'Chrissie…' Unable to cope with her sister's wretchedness right then, Kendal didn't know what to do. And Matthew, distressed by the situation and all the sobbing going on around him, was crying too. Only Jarrad, she realised, retained any degree of control.

He couldn't get to Matthew. Neither could he reach Kendal, which was, she could see in his eyes, all he wanted to do—not with her sister clinging desperately to his lower legs. He therefore did the only thing he could and reached down to catch the younger girl gently by the arm.

'Get up, Chrissie.' His voice was firm, yet surprisingly controlled in view of the tumultuous emotion slashing lines into the hard olive tones of his face. 'No one's going to hurt you.' Somehow he had got Chrissie to her feet, was urging her into one of the comfortable chairs beside the fireplace.

'How—how did—did you—find me?' Chrissie's words were broken by her sobs.

'Something Ralph said.'

Jarrad's clipped declaration made Chrissie look up to where he stood now, towering over her.

'Ralph?' The barest glimmer shone through the dark desolation in her eyes.

'He couldn't get in touch with you. He was worried sick! It seemed to be the only conclusion that it was you who had Matthew.'

There was silence for a moment. Then Chrissie dragged in a breath.

'I'm sor—ry, Kendal.' Her body was still shaken by deep and convulsive sobs. 'I didn't mean to take him.'

'Then why did you?' Kendal could only shake her head incredulously as she subsided onto the chair opposite her sister, cradling Matthew possessively in her arms. 'Why did you do it, Chrissie?'

'I don't know.' She looked timorously at Jarrad, who was standing with his hands planted almost threateningly on his hips in front of her, and burst into another fit of uncontrollable sobs.

'When I saw him that day,' she began, when she could speak again, 'and he ran over to me… I don't know what came over me. One minute he was there…and the next minute I'd picked him up and was driving away. I didn't stop and think about the pain I might be causing to you and Jarrad. I didn't give it a thought. But afterwards…after I'd stopped and thought about it…it was too late. I knew I couldn't keep him. I wanted to give him back, but I thought I'd be put in prison if I did. I thought I'd never see him…see any of you again…'

'Why the devil did you go there in the first place, Chrissie?' Jarrad's voice was strung with tangible restraint.

More restraint than she could begin to look for, Kendal realised as, with all the anguish she and Jarrad had suffered during the harrowing days that Matthew had been missing, she demanded, 'Didn't you give a single thought to us? His parents? Think about how either of us might feel?'

Her unavoidably sharp words caused Chrissie to visibly recoil, her small face to tighten beneath the short, spiky crown of her hair.

'Not at first,' she admitted after a moment. 'Anyway, you were always working.' Her words were directed accusingly at Kendal. 'Even when I was a teenager you were too busy working or studying to take any real interest in me. And now you're doing the same with Matthew!'

'Chrissie, you know that's an unfair thing to say.' Jarrad's tone was coolly chastising, causing Kendal to look up at his strong, dark profile in confusion.

He was defending her? When all along he was the one

who had complained about how much time she gave to her career?

'You know Kendal only worked and studied hard to give you the things other children had.'

Rebuked, Chrissie looked down at her sodden tissue which was starting to disintegrate between her nervous fingers, peppering her black cotton leggings with white specks.

'It was after that row with Ralph,' she rambled on, in a rather disjointed fashion. 'He said he'd never agree to us having anyone else's child. He made me feel as though I'd caused so many people a lot of trouble just through my wanting a baby. Did you know that that money he took wasn't for himself? That he borrowed it—got himself sacked—because of me?'

She was looking desolately up at Jarrad, who darted a sideways glance in Kendal's direction.

Kendal frowned. What money? Chrissie wasn't making sense.

'Haven't you told her?' Chrissie persisted, and now something of the old, familiar awe she had always displayed for Jarrad Mitchell showed through her tear-filled brown eyes.

'Told me? Told me what?' Kendal pressed, looking from Jarrad to her sister then back to Jarrad again.

'No, I didn't realise that—not until Ralph told me himself this morning,' Jarrad enlightened Chrissie, ignoring her second question—as well as Kendal's—to answer the first. 'When we found out he'd been dipping into company funds he begged me not to tell anyone—least of all you, his wife. I didn't realise he had.' He sounded annoyed for some reason.

'He didn't. Not until we were in Italy,' Chrissie chipped in, sensing the sudden change in his mood.

'He didn't, however, come clean about why he'd... borrowed it,' he said stiffly. 'That he'd used it to take you away on that cruise because of the state you were in after you'd suffered that second miscarriage, that he was up to his eyes in debt. When I asked him at the time if he had any financial difficulties he wouldn't admit to anything—least of all the state his marriage was in. Consequently, when we let him go, I didn't know the reasons behind his actions, or that you were pregnant.'

Because Chrissie hadn't told anyone—not even Ralph, Kendal remembered. It was something that Chrissie had wanted to share only with her older sister, afraid as she had been that something would go wrong again—as it ultimately had.

'Is that why you took Matthew, Chrissie?' Jarrad's voice had gentled a little. 'To pay me back in some way for being responsible—as you thought—for the loss of your own baby?'

Kendal flinched, grasping Matthew tightly even though he was struggling to get down. Arms outstretched, wanting to get back to his bricks, he suddenly started to wail.

Dear God! Hadn't she accused him of exactly that at Chrissie's that very morning? she remembered. This man whose baby she held so possessively to her and whose brutality—as she'd always thought it—in getting rid of her brother-in-law after he'd been caught so incriminatingly with Lauren, had instead been prompted by some unethical act committed by Ralph himself!

It would have been easy for Ralph, she supposed, being the company accountant, to help himself to the firm's money. And Jarrad had always stressed that there had been other reasons for her brother-in-law's dismissal besides the one he had given her about Ralph not pulling his weight. She hadn't accepted that anyway, hadn't believed him. But there was still Lauren, she reminded herself bitterly, even as another part of her commended him for not betraying Ralph to his family.

'No. I didn't want any sort of revenge on you, Jarrad.' Kendal was brought back to the present to hear Chrissie speaking. 'I've always liked you. I always believed you had good reasons for sacking Ralph even if Kendal didn't. But when he told me what he'd done, and that it was for me, I couldn't believe it. I hadn't realised that my wanting a baby so much—the way I was—could have driven him to do what he did and cost him his job. I wanted to make it all up to him, but then we had that row about adopting if I couldn't…'

She hung her small, dark, elfin head. 'Well, you know. When I came back on my own I felt so wretched. Worthless. Other women have babies and I… All I wanted was someone I could really care for—who I knew would really need and care for me. I knew Matthew needed someone. I drove up to town that day, and whether it was deliberate or not I don't know, but I found myself driving past the house where Kendal told me she took him—just in the hope of getting a glimpse of him.

'I saw him playing in the garden so I parked the car and went back and called him over. I couldn't believe it when he held out his arms to be picked up. The lady who was looking after him had her back to me—talking to another little boy—and she didn't see me. Before I knew it I'd grabbed him. It was all so easy. I didn't think beyond the next few days. Or even the next few hours. Afterwards, though, when I was here on my own, I got scared.'

The eyes she lifted to Jarrad's were dark with an appeal for understanding. 'I was hoping you'd find me. I didn't know what to—'

She broke off, her expression changing to one of panic as the mobile phone Jarrad always carried suddenly started to ring.

He took it from his trouser pocket, snapped up the cover. 'Mitchell, here.'

Who was it? The office? Kendal thought, astounded, wondering how he could possibly turn his mind to business at a time like this.

'Yes,' she heard him saying. 'Yes, she's safe. So is Matthew.' Then, 'No, no, we'll bring her home.'

'Was...that the police?' Chrissie asked, looking scared as Jarrad snapped the phone closed again.

'No, Ralph.'

'Ralph?' Both girls spoke in unison.

'He's just leaving the airport—on his way to Chrissie's. I told him to wait for us there,' he said softly to Kendal.

'Oh, no!' Chrissie sounded desperate. 'He isn't going to want me when he realises what I've done!'

Jarrad swung back to face her. 'Don't you think he already knows?' It seemed to Kendal he was having a battle now restraining the harshness in his voice. 'Surprisingly he apparently does!'

Chrissie gazed down at her speckled leggings, at the ragged tissue she was still twisting in her lap. 'Will I have to go to prison?' Though she wasn't looking at him, her question was for Jarrad alone.

Kendal caught her breath, remembering the words he'd uttered that morning at her sister's house—'I'll do what I have to.' But would he?

Unable to contemplate it, unconsciously she closed her eyes, clinging to Matthew who, for the moment, had stopped struggling and was content with tugging at her hair.

Unbelievably, Kendal heard him saying, 'I'll do my best to see that that doesn't happen, Chrissie. I can't press charges against my own sister-in-law. But you do need help, and I will insist that you get it, as I'm sure any court would if they were dealing with you. I'll help you all I can, but you must promise me you'll do everything necessary to co-operate.'

Meekly, Chrissie nodded, and then burst into tears again. But they were tears of relief this time, Kendal suspected, unable to take her eyes off Jarrad, unable to believe he was being so lenient with her sister after the cold-blooded way she had always believed he had treated Ralph.

Neither of them took much notice when Chrissie murmured something about finding some more tissues. Blue eyes were inextricably locked with green. And now Kendal sensed that wire-tight masculine restraint begin to release itself with the weary sagging of those wide shoulders. She was unable to believe how deeply the strain that he had obviously been under for the past few days had scored his face, giving an even more severe cast to his austere features.

'Thank you,' was all she could whisper as her sister's dragging footsteps sounded over the stairs. But he merely shrugged in response, because he was looking at Matthew, his face softening a little as he watched his son bouncing up and down, wanting to play, stamping energetically on his mother's lap.

'Let me hold him.'

The tremor in his voice made her look up quickly, but she passed Matthew over, her heart swelling as he caught the boy to him, holding him close, his face against the juncture of his baby's neck and tiny shoulder.

Matthew was crooning something in surprised recognition of his father's arms, but it was Jarrad that Kendal was looking at, seeing an emotion she had never expected to see.

His eyes were closed, so tightly that his pain was almost palpable, and the hands that clutched his son were rigid with tension. And he was shaking.

Unbelievably, he was crying, and, torn by the sight of such deep, masculine emotion, Kendal rose and went over to him, putting her arms around him, around them both.

It escaped him then, one deep, shuddering sob—because of course she had given in to her emotions when he had remained in control, when he had been the strong one, taking care of her, bringing her to Matthew, handling Chrissie.

I love you, she wanted to say as she dipped her head against his shoulder. I love you both. But she had done that before and he had thrown her love back in her face, and, whatever else they had been through since, it didn't alter the fact that he had wanted Lauren for whatever reason, even if he didn't want her now.

Perhaps she had driven him to it. Who knows? she wondered bleakly—putting him second because of her job. Even Chrissie had said she was always working. So perhaps she was as responsible for her sister's problems as she was for her own marriage falling apart, she considered, although she knew that that was being rather hard on herself, if not just a little bit self-pitying too. She knew she wasn't entirely to blame.

Saying nothing at all, she stayed, holding them both, until she felt the tremors leave that strong, masculine body, until she felt him gaining control again.

'So you do have some compassion, Kendal. Even for a man you profess to hate.' He lifted his head and looked at her with that same irony twisting his lips as had infiltrated his words. 'What have I suddenly done to deserve this?'

He was thoroughly in command of himself again, and, disconcerted by her own weakness for him—and for allowing him to see it—she let her arm fall away from him. Anyway, Matthew was starting to grizzle, twisting his little body so that he could hold his arms out to her. Gratefully, she took him, glad that the diversion had relieved her of answering his father because she wouldn't have known what to say.

It seemed natural, putting Matthew to bed in his old room that night, with its patchwork beanbags and fancy blue soldier wallpaper.

He didn't seem to have suffered in any way during the time that he'd been away, but both she and Jarrad stayed with him until he was asleep, snuggled up with his favourite blue teddy.

'You didn't tell me about Ralph,' Kendal said, sitting beside the cot, speaking in a lowered, almost wounded voice.

'No.' It was a heavily sighed response from the ottoman where Jarrad lounged easily, looking tired but relaxed.

'Why not?' she queried, absently stroking the appealing features of a cuddly toy sheep she was holding.

She had wanted to ask him when they had been driving back from Cumbria late that afternoon, but it had seemed impolitic to do so with Chrissie in the car.

'For exactly the reason I gave. He asked me not to,' he reiterated quietly. 'Would it have made any difference to your leaving me if I had?'

No, but I wouldn't have despised you in quite the way I did, Kendal thought, surprising herself, because hadn't he sought refuge in another woman's arms? And nothing could ever lessen the pain of that.

She shook her head.

'Exactly.' He had been sitting with his hands behind his head, leaning against the wall, but sat forward now, fixing her with the hard intensity of his gaze. 'My...close association with Lauren. Or, as you prefer to call it, my sensational affair! But no matter what you think of me, Kendal, even you can't destroy what there was—what there is— between us. Last night proved that.'

Her nails sank into the soft woollen toy as a blaze of heat stole across her cheeks. 'Last night I wasn't responsible for anything I did!' she uttered fiercely.

'I see.'

Did he? She hoped not. The smallest inkling of how she really felt about him, and he would play on her emotions for all he was worth!

'No, you don't!' she retorted, louder than she had intended.

Under the bedclothes, Matthew gave a little groan and stirred, and Kendal took a deep breath, striving to stay in control.

'Wouldn't it be better to continue this conversation downstairs?' Jarrad suggested. He hadn't needed to raise his voice at all.

'There's nothing to continue,' Kendal whispered without

looking at him. She was looking at Matthew; she didn't want to wake him.

'In that case,' he said, getting up and stretching so that her eyes were drawn reluctantly to the long, lean length of him beneath the fresh casual clothes he had changed into after driving back, 'don't sit up too long. It's late…and you haven't exactly had an easy day of it yourself.'

Which was an understatement, she thought, silently acknowledging his concern.

It had been a traumatic day all round, what with that first, shocking realisation that Chrissie had come back, that it was possibly—unbelievably!—her own sister who had taken Matthew, without being on the road for all that time as well. Then there had been the emotional reunion with Matthew—that first moment when she had caught him up in her arms, holding him close, the feeling that he was safe, hers again at last. Strangely, now though, only a matter of hours later, it was almost as though none of it had really happened, as though the whole past, agonising week had been nothing more than a terrible dream. Then there had been that moment when she had handed him to Jarrad…

With a lump in her throat she remembered the heart-wrenching intensity with which he had cradled his son, the emotion he had been unable to contain, her own realisation of how much she still loved him.

Well, of course she did, she accepted, otherwise she could never have given herself to him so completely and unashamedly as she had last night.

She had to struggle to ignore that throb of familiar tension deep down inside her from remembering how desperate they had been for each other, the ecstasy no other man had ever come close to making her feel. It would be so easy to go along with what he was expecting of her—to take up the role of his wife again and have the pleasure of his lovemaking always, the contentment and roused anticipation that came with waking up in his bed.

Even Chrissie had asked the question—after that other

emotional scene when she had been reunited with Ralph, who had been waiting for her at the house. Emotional because after Jarrad had telephoned the police to inform them that Matthew had been found, Ralph's promise to Chrissie to stand by her whatever happened had reduced both girls to tears—though for different reasons, Kendal decided now. Chrissie's tears had been simply out of sheer joy in securing the support of the man she loved, while her own had been for her sister's future, her happiness, and with hope that everything was going to turn out all right.

Chrissie had thrown her arms around her then, and had sobbed her apologies for all she had put her through, prompting her older sister to accept her remorse with something that served as a consoling embrace—because until then, feeling only numbness and the immeasurable relief of having her baby back, Kendal hadn't been able to make the move.

But it was afterwards, as she'd been leaving the house with Jarrad, she remembered, that her sister had posed her hopeful question. 'Are you guys back together? I've always wanted you to get back together.'

'Yes,' Jarrad had affirmed before Kendal could say anything.

Caught off-guard, shaken by his bold assertion, she had swiftly been compelled to tag on, 'For now.'

He hadn't made any comment, either then or later, and she wondered, as she slid down onto the rug with her back against the pale baby chest beside the cot, whether he had accepted that she just wouldn't simply fall back into the role she had once played just because of one moment of weakness the previous night—that things could never be the same as they had been before.

She must have fallen asleep, there on the rug with her head resting against the bars of the cot, because suddenly she was aware of someone gently shaking her.

'It's time you were in bed.' Jarrad's voice broke softly

through her bemused senses, and she groaned, opening her eyes.

From the small lamp burning beside the cot she saw that he was wearing only a dark towelling robe that exposed his hair-furred chest and powerful legs.

Her arm was stiff from where it had been curled around Matthew's dark head and, remembering, quickly she sat up, her breath leaving her in a gush. He was still safe. Still asleep. Still there with her. She hadn't just dreamt that he was back.

'You can't stay here all night.' Jarrad's voice was quietly admonishing. 'You're dead beat.' His hands were firm and warm under her elbows as gently he drew her to her feet. 'Come on. Come to bed,' he said in those deep, hushed tones.

She allowed him to lead her along to the large bedroom, even to slip open the buttons of her blouse and unfasten her skirt. But when she had divested herself of her undies and virtually crawled under the duvet, too tired even to put on a nightie, she realised with a shock that Jarrad had abandoned his robe and was sliding in beside her.

'What are you doing?' she breathed, startled by the accidental brush of his leg against hers.

'What do you think I'm doing? Coming to bed,' he whispered thickly, claiming his share of the duvet that she was clutching to her like a protective shield.

'Why?' she enquired, feeling too weary to put up any sort of battle against him. 'Do you think what happened between us here last night somehow renews your licence to share my bed?'

'I wasn't of the opinion my licence ever expired,' he drawled, talking literally, she hoped, although she thought he sounded amused. He couldn't possibly pretend his behaviour with Lauren hadn't revoked it entirely! 'We're still married, Kendal, and if you're going to stay here then it would be ludicrous to imagine we could settle for anything less than the normal husband/wife relationship we had before.'

Or he would sue for custody? He hadn't said that, not in those exact words, but he had intimated as much that morning. Because he loved Matthew every bit as much as she did—she had realised that today—and she wasn't sure whether he wouldn't try and keep her with him by executing his original threat. And if he did she didn't know whether she'd be strong enough—or even if it would be right after all that had happened—to put herself, or Matthew, through an emotional tug-of-war like that.

'No, not as it was before,' he added then. 'Because this time you're going to learn to trust me.'

'Am I?' she murmured bleakly, and shuddered from the sensations that assailed her as his warm hand shaped the smooth dip between her ribcage and her hip.

'Relax,' he breathed soporifically, and his hand stilled, though its warmth continued to burn into her flesh. 'What sort of man would I be—other than the type you clearly think I am—if I took you now, without a thought for how you were feeling? Because, darling, you've never been able to accuse me of that.'

No, he was right, she thought, because he was—and always had been—the most considerate of lovers. Except perhaps for the previous evening when neither of them had been able to maintain enough control in the inferno of passion that had consumed them.

'Go to sleep,' she heard him whisper.

She wouldn't have thought it was possible, but she must have fallen asleep almost immediately, lulled by his voice, still with that warm arm around her midriff, fatigue extinguishing the kindling desire that, had he chosen to, he could so easily have fanned into life.

CHAPTER EIGHT

I⊤ WAS barely light when Kendal awoke, disturbed by the sound of Jarrad moving about the room.

'What time is it?' she queried, frowning through the half-light.

'Early.' His tone was wry as he unfastened the dark robe he was wearing. 'I heard a sound and went to see if Matthew was OK.'

Kendal sat up with a start. 'And is he?' Anxiety laced her voice.

'Fine. He's sleeping like a log.'

'I must go and see him.' She was already throwing back the duvet.

'Leave him.' A strong hand was on her shoulder. 'He'll wake soon enough,' he said gently, though with a hoarseness to his voice that brought all her instincts of self-survival rushing to the fore.

'Jarrad…' It was a trembling protest as he pressed her back onto the mattress. 'Jarrad, don't.' She was startlingly conscious of her nakedness, and of his now that he had discarded the towelling robe.

'Jarrad, do.' His head came down, and very gently he kissed the corner of her mouth.

'No, I can't I—'

'Why can't you? Have you found someone else who turns you on more than I do? This Tony whatever-his-name-is, perhaps?'

Kendal sucked in her breath as his lips traced her jaw, her neck, the pulsing hollow that was hammering crazily at the base of her throat. It would be so easy to lie.

'No.' Something beyond candour urged her into telling him the truth.

'You were going away with him.'

Kendal's breath shivered through her as those lips touched the outer curve of her breast.

'No, I wasn't.'

'I see.' There was a tremor in his voice too. 'You only wanted me to think that.'

Had she? At that precise moment, with his mouth caressing the underside of her breast, she couldn't think of anything at all!

'Jarrad. This isn't fair...'

He chuckled low in his throat. 'Everything is in love and war. So what's it to be between us, Kendal?'

'Was there ever any difference?' she breathed, hating herself for loving what he was doing to her. War made a prisoner of its captives, and so did love. But where was the dignity of the captive who gloried in her bonds?

'For you—maybe not,' he said huskily. 'What are you trying to prove to me? Convince yourself of? That making love with me is only excusable when anger's driven you out of control?'

As it had last night? Or was it the night before? She couldn't think straight because her head was swimming, her body tensing at the exquisite torture as he lifted the full, throbbing weight of her other breast.

Dear heaven! What was she allowing to happen?

He knew what he was doing to her, knew too how much her mind rejected it, although he could see from the blossoming peaks of her breasts—caressed by the pale light filtering through the curtains—how much they craved his touch.

'Go now, darling.' His breathing was ragged and his mouth played tantalisingly across their burgeoning fullness, planting kisses around the dark aureoles while leaving them achingly bereft. 'Go now, or you stay with me, Kendal.'

Oh, how could he do this to her?

She dragged in a breath, tried to speak and couldn't because his tongue was tracing a moist path down the silken valley between her breasts while his hands splayed out beneath them. But she hesitated too long, and when his mouth closed over one sensitised peak she felt the flame of hunger ignite deep down inside of her, and she was lost again.

Her shuddering sob came from the depths of her lungs as she abandoned herself to the pleasure—the pleasure of giving and taking, touching him, feeling him caressing her. And it was with a calculated dedication, she realised almost unbearably at once, because this morning he was infinitely tender.

This morning the depth of his control seemed to know no bounds, and the sweet torture of his lovemaking seemed eternal.

'Please...' She heard herself begging as her legs spread out beneath him, small beads of perspiration breaking out on her pale skin as she waited, sobbing her need, her breath leaving her on a sharp, guttural sound as finally he granted her wish and claimed the glorious gift of her body.

Release was all she craved now, her slender body racked with need. But he was in no hurry, his subsequent withdrawal after each controlled thrust not the actions of the starving man who had devoured her hungrily that other night, but of the gourmet who, having seasoned his banquet with all the flavourings of his experience, was determined to savour it to the last.

When eventually he lost control, she was already over the brink, the warm flow of him inside of her a balm to soothe the throbbing spasms of her own flowering femininity.

And some time afterwards release produced the inevitable remorse.

Lying in the curve of his shoulder, thinking him asleep, she tensed as he suddenly reached up and touched her cheek.

'What the—?' The word he used was unrepeatable as he retracted his fingers, moist with her tears. 'You're crying.'

Kendal caught her breath. 'No, I'm not.'

'Don't lie to me.' He raised himself up on an elbow. There was a dewy dampness to his skin. 'Why are you crying?' he demanded to know, those hard features touched with concern.

She couldn't answer him, because she didn't really know herself. Was it just emotion produced by the physical release she had craved and found almost too much to cope with when it had come? Or a profound effect of the intensity of her feelings for this man that could never be denied no matter what he did?

She suspected the latter, but she couldn't tell him that. She wondered if her mother had felt the same degree of powerless resignation when she had reconciled herself to the fact that she could never live without Robert Harringdale, and had taken her unfaithful husband back into her bed.

'No reason,' she uttered instead, dragging her gaze away from that masculine chest before she gave into the urge to run her aching fingers through that triangle of dark hair.

'Don't be ridiculous! There has to be a reason!'

'I'm all right,' she stressed more firmly now. 'Why can't you leave it like that?'

That hard mouth pulled down at one side. 'Because I want you to be happy. I want us both to be happy.'

'Aren't you?' She sniffed back her tears, the adrenalin produced by arguing with him helping to bring her emotions back under control again. 'You've got what you wanted.'

'And what's that?'

She directed her glance to the curtains—beyond which she could see the sun was now fully risen—before defeat, born out of her weakness for him, urged her into saying, 'Matthew and me—back where you wanted us, in your life again.'

'So that's it.' He rolled onto his back with a heavily released breath. 'And what about what you want? Or do you get some warped kick out of playing the martyr? Convincing yourself you'd rather not be here? Is that what all the tears are about? Regret?'

No, they're because I love you! She wanted him to realise that, but sank her teeth into her lower lip for fear of crying it out. She would never, never lay herself open to such stark vulnerability with him, as her mother had done with her father. Never let him know how deeply her feelings ran or he would realise, just like Robert Harringdale had, how big a fool for him his wife was.

'I'm not exactly of the opinion that you made love with me under total sufferance this morning,' he rasped thickly, turning to look at her when she remained silent. 'Or that I was enjoying it all by myself!'

The sun made a blaze of her hair as she turned her head away. 'That's just chemistry,' she lied.

'Is that all it is?' he asked roughly, sitting up and catching her chin between his thumb and forefinger, forcing her to look at him, to meet the depths of naked hunger in his eyes.

Oh, God! How can I carry on like this when I love you so much? she thought harrowingly, closing her eyes so that he wouldn't see the dark emotion that could so easily have betrayed her.

Some deep-rooted need to survive urged her into speech. 'I agreed to come back—for Matthew's sake—not to sleep with you. But you want it all, don't you?'

'Yes!' It was a huskily breathed admission. 'I don't see how you can agree to stay if you're not prepared to try and make our marriage work—if you're only going to settle for half-measures. But if that's all you've got to give then let's make the most of it, shall we?'

'No!' Her protest was a small sob as the weight of his warm, sweat-slicked body came down heavily on hers, pinning her to the bed. His kiss was almost brutal, and the coarse hair of his chest was a stimulating friction against her breasts, which were still sensitive from his earlier caresses.

No, please don't let him prove that he can still take me. Not like this! her mind raged, already succumbing to the sharpening thrill of her ravaged senses. But with a sudden, tangible condemnation, he pulled roughly away from her as though he despised himself—leaving her, contrarily, aching from the loss of his nearness as he threw back the covers and got up.

During the days that followed the recovery of Matthew, the Press were like hungry hyenas who, having been thrown a good meal, lurked in wait outside the house for any other scraps of human suffering they could devour.

Kendal would have preferred not to have spoken to them at all. In fact, the only interview she gave was to a seemingly understanding young woman whose gentle persuasion—rather than the dogged persistence she had met from other reporters—finally urged her into expressing that she felt no animosity towards her sister whatsoever. When asked to comment on how she had felt when she had discovered that it was her sister who had taken her child, she replied simply, 'Shocked.'

But when the woman, sensing that she had gained Kendal's confidence, asked whether her reconciliation with her husband had occurred as a direct result of her baby's abduction, she refused to comment. Anything to do with Jarrad and herself was personal and private. She had no intention of discussing her marriage with the rest of the world.

The fact was that very little had changed since she had walked out of his life over a year ago. Though Lauren's name scarcely intruded upon their conversation these days, and Jarrad spent very little time away from home, the past still hung between them like a dark curtain.

He had moved back into the spare room after that morning he had found her crying after their lovemaking. And, though the impact of their physical chemistries couldn't be denied, the tension that each produced in the other was contained behind a mutual, stretched reserve. That was until repressed emotion strained them to their limits, and then it escaped in sheer, unadulterated anger.

At least, though, he protected her from all the unwanted media attention, Kendal realised gratefully as he swiftly dispensed with the persistent journalists in a cool but effective way in which she knew she could never have succeeded.

She didn't even know to what extent the papers had covered the story of her baby's disappearance—or what they had made of it—and she didn't want to know, didn't even attempt to read them. She only knew that in some way it was partly her fault that Chrissie had taken Matthew.

That was a natural feeling, she remembered her sister's therapist saying. A mother always blamed herself, no matter what the circumstances of the abduction.

The other woman didn't know, though, to what boundaries the extent of her guilt stretched—guilt about leaving Jarrad, guilt that in some way she hadn't done her best for Chrissie, guilt for placing too much importance on her career—which she had since abandoned along with her dreary little flat—and, most of all, for perhaps neglecting Matthew.

Guilt burned into her like a searing knife, but bravely she dealt with the emotion alone. Too much time had already been wasted in anguish and self-recrimination. If nothing else, that week without Matthew had taught her how precious time and his babyhood was to her, and, as the weeks passed, along with the summer, and she saw how quickly he was growing up, she knew how swiftly his childhood would be gone.

'You'll be a man before we know it, won't you?' she chuckled at him one mellow morning, squatting down to where he was playing with his tricycle on the patio to feed him another small piece from a chocolate flake she had bought for them both as a rare treat.

'More!' he exclaimed, dragging a chocolatey finger down his cheek. In fact there was chocolate everywhere. Around his mouth, over his hands, and where he had dribbled all down the front of his clean blue dungarees.

'I think you've had quite enough already.'

Amusement tinged Jarrad's deep voice as he came along the path from the direction of the kitchen, causing Kendal's pulse to leap as she hadn't seen him since the day before yesterday. She couldn't look at him, however, beyond one brief glance that registered his lean elegance in a pale blue polo shirt and light trousers, still shamed as she was by the humiliation she had endured at his hands the last time they had met.

They had had another row about Lauren—about the time he'd been going to spend away last night—and he had told Kendal that it was a problem that was all in her own mind. It had become so ugly that she had finished up by tossing the contents of a glass of wine at him. She recoiled from the degradation that remembering it brought—the shame she'd known instantly at such a gross lack of control. But she had paid for it. Oh, God, had she paid for it!

In the seconds that it took him to cross to the patio, she remembered his savage anger as he'd dragged her down onto the settee, the sensual onslaught with which he had had her sobbing for the only thing that had seemed to matter—then only to abandon her, leaving her with the knowledge that she had compromised all her principles, and he with the triumph of having known that she would.

'More!' Matthew persisted now, and mentally Kendal shook herself back to the present, to see her son waving urgent little hands at her as he always did when he wanted his own way.

'I'm sorry, Matthew. But it's all gone.' She held up her hands with the empty wrapping, and, because she could see his little face crumpling, added unintentionally sharply, 'Look! It's all gone!'

'More,' Matthew whimpered, looking appealingly to his father this time.

'You heard her, Matthew.' He held up his hands—long, tanned hands that had wrung that humiliating submission from her two nights ago, and which sent a sensual shudder through her at the memory. 'All gone.'

Ten sticky brown fingers uncurled themselves and were held, palms outward, to Jarrad.

'All goh!' Matthew repeated, with a big smile for his father now.

'That's it, son.' Jarrad stooped to ruffle Matthew's dark, silky hair. 'You've got the message.' But his glance strayed to Kendal, and she felt his eyes touch on the open V of her blouse which she had only just realised was gaping enough to reveal the pale upper swell of one breast.

'Perhaps you should be here all the time. He obviously listens to you!' she snapped, irritable with herself for speaking so sharply to Matthew and for being so affected by Jarrad—which was really what had brought it about.

'I'm glad someone does around here,' he drawled, straightening at the same time as Kendal shot to her feet.

'Meaning?' God! Why were they always quarrelling?

'I really don't think you'd welcome hearing it, Kendal.'

'Why not?' she pressed, remorse and guilt and her shaming desire for him all coalescing in a searing vortex to hurt her inside. 'Let's have another hour of punishing Kendal, shall we?'

A breeze sweeping through the cedar tree whipped her bright curls as she faced him belligerently, loving him and at the same time hating him. Hating him especially for this intensity of emotion she couldn't deny for him even if he had had a thousand Laurens, even if her very life had depended upon it.

'Haven't you had enough?'

His softly aimed snipe effectively silenced her, bringing

wings of hot colour up across her cheeks. So that was what her capitulation to him had been the other night—a punishment, she realised, humiliated, despairing with herself for the warped stimulation even that remark produced as she felt desire kick hard, deep in her loins.

'Come on. Let's get this little lad cleaned up.' He was scooping Matthew up into his arms, ignoring Kendal, though he had to be fully aware of, if not rejoicing in her chagrin. 'I thought we'd all go down to the coast together—unless, of course, you'd care to suggest something else.'

Kendal swallowed, wanting to be with Matthew, welcoming a day by the sea. And yet the degradation she was experiencing from his father's cruel reminder of how easily he could use her—just as her mother had allowed herself to be used by Kendal's own father—wouldn't permit her even to be tempted by his offer.

'I've got a hairdresser's appointment,' she told him nonetheless, but lamely, having deliberately arranged it for the weekend. Deliberately, not so much because of the party that Jarrad was throwing that evening to celebrate his management team's effort in securing the American contract, but so that they wouldn't have to endure too much of each other's company before then. But, telling herself that what was best for Matthew was what really counted, without wanting to appear to climb down completely, she added, 'You should have told me. I suppose I could always try and postpone it...' His concurrence was all she was waiting for to do just that.

'Don't bother,' he snarled then, making her realise—and with surprising self-admonition—that he had probably persuaded her once too often. 'I prefer you when you've got less to say and more to offer! When we don't have to be civil or pretend even to like each other—between the sheets!'

And, with that scorching remark, he took Matthew and walked away.

The sound of water in the drain beneath the kitchen win-

dow brought her attention to the fact that Teeny was standing at the sink, and she caught the woman's reproving
glance as she wandered back into the house.

'You're going to lose him, Kendal,' she expressed, making her shamefully aware that Teeny had heard every word
she'd exchanged out there with Jarrad. 'You're pushing him
to the limit, and if this wasn't his house it wouldn't surprise
me if one day he didn't pick up Matthew and go.'

Teeny was busy preparing food for the party that evening, washing her hands from shelling a bowlful of suc-
culent-looking pink prawns that stood on one side of the
sink.

'What do you know about it?' Kendal challenged, smarting from the woman's rather chastening remarks.

'Only what I see. And I see a man at the end of his
tether,' she uttered, defending Jarrad. 'You're the one
who's punishing—punishing him, Kendal—and not for
anything he's done as far as I can see. Only for what you
think he's done. And that isn't good enough.'

'What right have you got—?' she began, startled by
Teeny's unexpected confrontation with her, but the housekeeper cut across her, shaking water off her large, capable
hands.

'The right of someone on the outside looking in.
Someone old enough to see what you're doing to each
other,' she added, reaching for a towel. She doted on
Jarrad—always had, Kendal suspected—and it was clear
she wasn't going to stop until she had said her piece.
'Avoiding each other. Sleeping in separate rooms. It's dis-
graceful! You haven't got a mother or a father, my girl,
and it's about time someone had a serious talk to you before
another marriage winds up unnecessarily in the divorce
courts. I know you think he cheated on you—'

'How do you know that?' She had never thought of
Teeny Roberts as a busybody or an eavesdropper, she realised, shocked.

The older woman pulled a face, wiping her hands. 'Don't

you think I haven't heard you shouting at each other? I like
to mind my own business and let other people mind theirs,
but it's a bit difficult when I hear two people who should
be enjoying their life together tearing each other apart. It's
no good for the boy, either, so something's got to be said.'

Having tossed down the towel, she scooped up the bowl
of redundant prawn shells and took them over to the waste-
bin.

'Did you think I didn't know the reason you broke up?
I might not have said anything before but I'm not deaf or
blind. I also happen to know Jarrad Mitchell better than I
know anyone—probably even better than you do, I
shouldn't wonder. That man's never been in love with anyone else. He wouldn't have gone to pieces the way he did
after you left him last year—drinking, working all hours,
cursing everybody for the least little thing—if he didn't
worship the ground you walk on.'

'Worship—?' Kendal broke off, unable to believe that
her leaving Jarrad could have affected him so profoundly—
although hadn't Lauren said something similar...? 'He just
wanted Matthew back and I was part of the package,' she
stated, as much for her own sake as the housekeeper's.

'If you're stubborn enough to believe that—then you
carry on,' Teeny remonstrated. 'They say people are totally
blind when it comes to their own lives. You're a very mature young woman in many ways. You've had to be to
bring up that sister of yours single-handed...'

And a fat lot of good I made of that! Kendal thought
with grimacing self-criticism before Teeny went on.

'You're warm and intelligent and very likeable, but
sometimes you can be so downright obstinate. You just
can't see where you're going wrong. You can't go on al-
ienating him the way you're doing, Kendal. If he were any
other man he'd—'

'Yes, what would I do, Teeny?'

Both women swung round, and Kendal stiffened, meeting Jarrad's inexorable mockery in the doorway.

'Oh, sir! I didn't know you were still in the house!'

Only Jarrad could make the practical Teeny blush, Kendal decided, before she heard that deep voice drawl again, 'Evidently not.' The smile he flashed at his housekeeper was one of warm indulgence as he conveyed to her, 'We'll be back before seven, Teeny.' But the eyes he turned on Kendal were cool, promising all sorts of things—and none of them good.

She stuck her chin out with a defiant little lift which he acknowledged with a tight smile before he went, without even bringing Matthew over for a kiss as he usually did before taking him out.

Tears bit behind her eyes as regret for the time she wouldn't be sharing with her son—and, surprisingly, her husband—filled her with self-chastening remorse.

'Yes, eat your heart out, girly,' she heard Teeny advising in that disapprovingly maternal tone of hers. 'You've brought it all on yourself. Now look where it's got you. From where I'm standing that man should have taken a firmer stand with you weeks ago.'

'Oh, Teeny, shut up!' Kendal cried, sweeping out of the kitchen, unable to take any more, because as far as she was concerned Jarrad Mitchell had everything he wanted.

Or was there some truth in what Teeny had just said? she was startled to find herself wondering as she ran up the stairs. Could it be possible that he'd never wanted Lauren Westgate? How could it be when she had found that restaurant slip for two breakfasts, and those hotel room bills? When her own brother-in-law had seen them together? She was being a fool if she let anyone make her believe anything else.

Nevertheless, as she stifled the doubts she wanted so badly to entertain, she knew an intensifying ache of regret at not swallowing her pride and going with him as she heard his car pull away.

She spent the rest of the morning and the afternoon trying to make the most of a few hours to herself, which usu-

ally she enjoyed. But today she just felt lonely and the day
seemed to have lost most of its glow.

She missed Matthew terribly, and, though she didn't like
admitting it to herself, she missed Jarrad too. She wondered
where he had taken the boy, and found it hurt to picture
them enjoying themselves without her—because they
would be enjoying themselves, of that she could be sure.

Whatever Jarrad might have done to her, he was a model
parent, and he threw himself into the role of fatherhood
with a relish that proved what a delight it was to him being
with Matthew rather than a duty. But then, he had always
been a good father, she thought, even before she had
packed her things and taken Matthew away.

For some reason today she appreciated the loss he must
have suffered more keenly than she had ever done before.
Even when Matthew had been taken from them both she
had been too steeped in her own grief to fully recognise
the distress to which she must have subjected Jarrad in refusing to let him see his son. Because that was what it had
amounted to in going into hiding as she had—deprivation—
and of his own flesh and blood.

But he had deserved it, hadn't he? she reminded herself
in defiance of Teeny's revelations to her that morning. He
was the one who'd been playing around, for heaven's sake!

So you made him pay—and in the cruellest possible way,
a nagging little voice inside persisted, goading her. Because
whatever quarrel you might have had with him, Matthew
was still his son.

Later, while sitting in the salon as the young girl finished
finger-drying her hair into a frenzy of red waves, Kendal
relived the pain and acute sense of injustice she had known
because of Lauren's intrusion upon her marriage. She had
thought it the ultimate agony, losing her husband to another
woman. But then there was that other anguish that could
be like no other.

The pain now was like a stab in the chest as she remembered the torture of losing her child. Had Jarrad experienced

that feeling twice? The first time—even though it might have been to a lesser degree—when she had taken Matthew away from him? Because no matter what he had done or how much he hurt you, her conscience continued to flay her, no loving parent deserves to go through that!

Paying the receptionist, Kendal shook off the disquieting and unwelcome thoughts she had been having since Teeny had taken her to task that morning, and, needing some company, she decided to call in to see her sister before she went home.

Fortunately, Chrissie had been spared the worst possible consequences of a prosecution. She had, however, spent weeks receiving treatment for her problems at a private psychiatric clinic.

Recently discharged, however—except on an out-patient basis—she seemed happier than she had in a long time, and, though still thin, had gained a little more weight, Kendal was pleased to notice, since she had seen her last.

'Ralph's going into the antique business, and he says we can move away—perhaps to the Lake District—when I don't have to attend the clinic any more,' Chrissie told her later, just as she was leaving. 'And if we can't have kids...' She shrugged her thin shoulders with sad but surprisingly mature acceptance. 'I might have screwed up my opportunity to adopt—I don't know. But who knows...?' She gave a wry little grimace. 'I'll just start a donkey farm or something!'

And you'll have Matthew. You'll always have Matthew, Kendal would liked to have said—would have said just a few months ago—but she couldn't now. Instead she hugged her sister with a heartfelt, 'That's my girl,' realising with a lump coming to her throat the precious gift of a child that she and Jarrad had been granted, and which, just a year ago, she had regarded simply as her right.

She was battling with emotion as she walked down Chrissie's path, and had to blink back tears as she came face to face with the sturdy young man who was just getting out of the dark blue saloon parked beside the kerb.

'So what do you think? She's doing all right, isn't she?'

Ralph looked happier, too, Kendal noted as he released her from his arms after the warm, friendly hug he had bestowed upon her.

'She looks great, Ralph.' Kendal smiled. 'Give or take a few pounds. That hospital certainly seems to have helped restore her confidence and her ability to cope with things again.'

'Yes, it does, doesn't it?' Ralph positively beamed. 'She's going to be OK.'

'Thanks to you.'

Ralph looked at her askance. 'Me?' he pretended to query innocently.

'Don't be so modest,' Kendal scolded warmly. 'You stuck by her at a time when she needed you most, and when it must have been jolly hard—and on top of that you provided her with the best possible treatment.'

Ralph shrugged. 'I just realised how much I loved her that day she walked out on me in Italy. But getting her into that clinic—well, I'm afraid I'm not exactly in a position yet to be able to provide private care like she got there. But I'll be able to give her everything she wants eventually—without getting into debt any more. I won't need to—now that Jarrad's put up some capital for my new venture. You know, this antiques thing...?'

Kendal nodded, trying not to look as dumbfounded as she was feeling. She couldn't tell him that she hardly knew anything about it at all, and what she did know she had only gleaned from Chrissie this afternoon. Couldn't tell him that it was impossible for her and Jarrad to communicate on any level—except perhaps in bed! But she didn't want to think about that.

'Obviously there has to be something in it for Jarrad, doesn't there?' she remarked sceptically. 'Otherwise why would he even consider helping his sister-in-law's husband with his new business?

'Well, of course there is,' Ralph returned without any hesitation or apparent malice. 'Jarrad's a businessman—and a darned good one. And that's an understatement.' He grimaced. 'The man's a phenomenon! Which is why I asked for his advice and jumped at the chance to have his backing when he suggested it.'

What could she say to that? There wasn't an up-and-coming business anywhere that wouldn't have welcomed Jarrad Mitchell's support, financial or otherwise!

'Of course it had to be on his terms,' Ralph told her, 'and I had a pretty strong lecture about ethics. But I think he wanted to see us—particularly your sister—back on her feet.'

'Then…if you weren't paying for Chrissie's therapy…?' Kendal started, unable to believe what she was suddenly thinking as Ralph came back in with a self-condemnatory snort.

'I'm afraid my pursestrings didn't stretch to that. It was Jarrad who funded it.' And then, 'I thought you knew,' he whispered, seeing the stunned incredulity on her face.

'It's all right, Ralph. I'm afraid we don't confide in each other very much these days,' she murmured ruefully, trying to ease his discomfiture.

'Things still not that good?' His voice was sympathetic against the sudden sound of a door slamming across the street. He glanced across, waving absently to the man, who waved back before getting into his car.

Kendal shook her head. What was the point of pretending? 'Just don't tell Chrissie,' she cautioned. 'She thinks we're getting on all right, and I don't want anything to upset her. Apart from which she thinks Jarrad's the best thing since sliced bread—next to you, of course—and that he can do no wrong. But she hasn't known many men, and—'

'And behind the charm we're all first-rate rogues—is that what you're trying to say?'

Now it was Kendal's turn to feel awkward. Her cheeks grew pink against the fire of her freshly shampooed hair.

'I—I didn't mean that,' she stammered, aware that Ralph had paid back every penny he had stolen from TMS when he had been its accountant—and with interest. Besides, although it didn't really excuse him, whatever he had done it had only been circumstances that had driven him to it, she thought, hoping he didn't think she had been implying anything untoward about him.

'Look,' he began, suddenly appearing as uncomfortable as she knew she must look. 'I've often felt rather bad about... Well, that perhaps it was partly my fault that you split up with Jarrad. I mean—that evening in the office when I saw him with Lauren...I might have interpreted things incorrectly...could have been wrong about what I saw.'

'Wrong? How could you have been wrong?' Kendal queried, flabbergasted. 'You either saw them or you didn't! You told me yourself you saw Lauren in his arms!'

'What I said was that I thought Lauren had her arms around him—there is a difference. No, what I mean is...' Ralph looked decidedly disconcerted now. 'Goodness, I'm bungling this! It was just this feeling I had. The way they stopped talking and looked so...well, guilty when I walked in. I thought they'd just pulled out of a lovers' embrace because they were standing pretty damn close—and I felt that Lauren in particular wanted me to know it. But I've realised since that they might have been talking confidentially and just shut up as soon as I walked in because they were talking about me. That would make some sense. Did Jarrad tell you what I did? About the money, I mean?'

Distractedly, Kendal shook her head. 'Not in so many words,' she uttered, remembering that it had been Chrissie who had first disclosed the information up there in that cottage. Yet another example of hers and Jarrad's inability to confide in each other, she thought. Then realised that perhaps it was more a further example of that integral and altruistic side to her husband's character—which she was only just beginning to know—which had kept him from telling her in the first place.

'You were so suspicious—so crazily in love with him— anything would have fired your imagination,' Ralph continued, unaware of the deep ache his words produced deep down inside Kendal. 'You didn't need me to throw any kindling on it. Anyway, those nights you thought they were spending away together—I realised afterwards that they were probably just off trying to sort out the mess I'd made of various deals they'd been trying to secure—win back the goodwill with various clients I'd upset.

'Things were so bad with Chrissie and me—I was drinking too much and making a real hash of things. Consequently I couldn't handle the people I had to deal with. I lost a lot of business for TMS, and I guess it took all Jarrad's and Lauren's joint efforts to win it back. I realised that afterwards, when I was sober and my head was clear enough to think. I also realised that I'd been wrong in letting you force out of me how much time they were spending together. I only know Jarrad's hard-headed and power-driven when it comes to business—but he does have morals.'

'Are you saying he never wanted Lauren?' she enquired bitterly.

Ralph shrugged. 'Has he said he did?'

Pain lined Kendal's brow as she stared sightlessly at the half-fastened zipper of her brother-in-law's casual jacket.

'He's only ever said I have to believe what I want to believe,' she admitted, considering for the first time how such a statement could just as easily reflect innocence as guilt.

'Proud to the last.' One side of Ralph's mouth cocked upwards. 'And he is proud, Kendal. Prouder than most. And with all that pride, if he's as principled as I think he is, he's never going to get down on his knees and beg you to believe him. He'd rather you took him for what he is. And if you can't then he'll see it as your weakness, not his.'

She couldn't believe this! And for the second time that day! No one was on her side. Not Teeny. Not even Ralph any more.

'But how will I ever know?' she uttered with despairing poignancy. Oh, God! If only she could believe...

Ralph shrugged again. 'I guess you'll just have to trust him, Kendal,' he said, giving her a swift peck on the cheek before turning away towards Chrissie who, having obviously seen him from the window, was waiting for him now by the front door.

Trust. Such a simple word to say. Yet encompassing such a world of tragedy and heartache in reality. Her mother had trusted, and that trust had cost her her life—her hopes and her dreams totally shattered by her husband's repeated infidelity.

So was she supposed to forget the hard lesson she had learned from watching her mother ultimately destroy herself? Wasn't she being prudent in refusing to accept anything that she couldn't prove for herself? Or had she simply been so badly affected by Robert Harringdale's behaviour, by her own parents' marriage, that she couldn't place any reliance on her own? Would it have been the same with any man she had married? Or just Jarrad? Because—heaven help her!—she loved him. So much!

Was she being wise in not allowing herself to go along wholeheartedly with everything he expected her to believe? Or were Ralph and Teeny right? Had she been a blind, suspicious fool? Because, if that was the case, then she hadn't ridden the storm of her parents' marriage—come through it and her mother's tragic death—as successfully as she had always prided herself on doing. She was just as emotionally mixed-up and battle-scarred because of it as Chrissie.

CHAPTER NINE

JARRAD was already back when Kendal arrived home. He was in the kitchen, taking something out of the fridge.

Her heart swelled with emotion as she observed him from the doorway, unnoticed, for a few moments as he stooped solicitously over Matthew, reaching down with a fruit drink to those tiny, extended arms.

Banking down emotion, she went in, crossing the cushioned vinyl floor.

'Did you have a good morning?' she asked briskly as he glanced up, keen to smooth over the earlier ill feeling between them.

Jarrad straightened, not altogether able to conceal his surprise at the effort she was making.

'Yes.' He sounded hesitant, wary. 'Did you?'

She nodded, tossing her bag down onto the table that matched the natural wood of the kitchen cabinets. 'Did you get to the seaside?'

'Sure did. In fact Matthew's got something for you, haven't you, Matt?'

Curious, Kendal frowned as Jarrad lifted him up, taking the now unwanted beaker from his tiny hands.

'What is it? What have you got?' she urged in tender anticipation.

Something rattled as Jarrad shook his shirt pocket and the little boy squealed with glee.

'For me?' Kendal smiled lovingly as one baby hand uncurled to expose the little shell his father had made it possible for him to extract from his breast pocket. The same procedure followed not once, not twice, but three times.

'Whose idea was this?' Kendal laughed, finding it difficult to meet Jarrad's disturbingly cool blue gaze.

'Let's say it was a joint venture,' he said smoothly, and now Kendal gave him a fleeting smile. So he had thought about bringing her something, even though he'd left her in the throes of a heated argument, she realised, surprised.

'No, that's it, Matthew,' he said, opening his raised palm to the little boy who was thumping energetically at his empty pocket.

Matthew stopped thumping and copied him. 'All goh!' he remembered with a gleeful smile.

'That's right, darling.' Kendal reached over to kiss the warm, baby softness of his temple. 'All gone,' she whispered, quickly pulling back when a movement from Jarrad caused that masculine jaw to accidentally brush against her hair, the familiar aftershave lotion he used to impinge upon her senses.

But then Teeny called to Matthew from the garden and Jarrad set him back on his feet, laughing with Kendal as the little boy looked back at them with a cheeky grin before toddling off to join Teeny outside.

'He seems happy,' Kendal couldn't help remarking.

'I'm not surprised,' Jarrad drawled.

She looked at him askance, a thin line knitting her brows.

'Well?' he said, and his voice was silkily seductive. 'Have you got one for his father?'

He meant a kiss, and her pulse went into overdrive as she saw the febrile glitter through the amusement in his eyes.

She wanted to, wanted to kiss him as much as she wanted to believe the things that Teeny and Ralph had told her. But his demonstration the other night of how easily he could wring a submission from her still rankled, and pointedly she reminded him, 'The last time you didn't need to ask!'

Beneath the pale blue shirt his chest expanded heavily.

'No,' he breathed, and she could tell from his sigh that he regretted his action now.

She hesitated, her throat working nervously as she reached out and touched his jaw with tentative fingers. It was coarse with new bristle, despite his shave first thing. Gingerly then she stood on tiptoe to kiss him lightly on one corner of his mouth.

'Oh, come on! You can do better than that!' He grinned, grabbing her wrist when she would have moved away.

She swallowed. 'What makes you think I want to?' she murmured, though he had to be able to feel the leaping of her pulse beneath the hard pressure of his thumb.

'This.' His other arm encircled her waist, pulling her lower body hard against his. Sagaciously his eyes raked over her face, reading the desire in her dilated pupils, in the shallowness of her breathing, in her distended nostrils—keen for the stimulating scent of him. 'Now kiss me properly,' he ordered.

He wasn't going to help her, but then he wasn't going to let her go either, and, tentatively now, she wound her arms around his neck and pressed her trembling lips against his.

His jaw felt delightfully coarse against her skin as her mouth moved over the firm stillness of his. But then he groaned, at the same time as she felt his body stir and harden, and the next instant he was taking over and her mouth was parting with mutual urgency beneath his.

When he broke the kiss for his lips to move with excruciating sweetness along her throat, she uttered a small, helpless sound and his hold relaxed a little, his head coming up with the subtlest lift of brows.

'You're pleasingly compliant—responsive today,' he murmured, his surprised amusement tempering the passion that hadn't yet altogether ensnared him in its power. 'I was beginning to think it would only take a full-scale row with me to ignite those fires.'

Because anger and passion often resulted in the same

thing, she thought—a total loss of control. And hiding behind the one somehow helped to salve her pride over succumbing so uncontrollably to the other—as she nearly had the night before last...

'Let me go,' she breathed shakily, because she couldn't begin to tell him what had happened to her today. How Teeny—and then Ralph—had started these doubts in her, shaming her into wondering if, by the slimmest chance, she had been wrong about him and Lauren—because she had been wrong about everything else. His treatment of Ralph. His handling of Chrissie. His unbelievable feeling for Matthew.

'If Teeny and Matt weren't outside and we didn't have this infernal party tonight you wouldn't have a chance,' he murmured, releasing her just as the alarm bell on the split-level oven announced that some delicious-smelling desserts had finished cooking and brought Teeny rushing in from outside.

'Now that only leaves the topping on the pavlova and those cheesecakes you made yesterday,' she said to Kendal, who was rescuing two superb-looking puddings from the oven. 'Oh, and the sauce for the prawn vol-au-vents,' she added, bustling around—enjoying herself, Kendal realised, even though the woman appeared rushed off her feet. When Jarrad had suggested getting caterers in, however, Teeny had put up horrified objections, and had also refused most of Kendal's help as well.

'Prawns always go down well,' Teeny crooned, clearly in her element with the way the puddings had turned out. 'Although none of it will probably be any good for Lauren.'

Kendal stiffened at the casual mention of the other woman's name. She should have realised, though, that as the party was primarily to celebrate TMS securing its most important contract to date, it was obvious that Lauren would be there.

'She won't eat anything with sugar, and she's always

been allergic to shellfish, she told me once. That's right, isn't it, sir?'

Kendal couldn't look at Jarrad as she slid the second glass pudding bowl onto the work surface to cool, only absently aware of the delicious lemony aroma rising, with the scent of hot raspberries and fresh sponge topping, on the steam. She wondered if he could tell how jittery she was, how her breathing seemed to have temporarily ceased.

'I haven't the faintest idea,' he drawled casually, as though it didn't matter to him one way or the other, as though he really didn't know! But wouldn't he know? Her mind raced hectically. If they had been close enough to be lovers! When you were that intimate with someone you wanted to know everything about them. And something like her food preferences would have been unavoidable, she reasoned. Unless, of course, he was merely purporting not to know...

'You surprise me,' she said quietly as Teeny hurried off to fetch something from the dining room.

'That will make a change,' he said drily, surveying one of his housekeeper's celebrated garlic dips and inhaling its pungent aroma with a grimace. 'Would it also surprise you,' he went on, turning round to lean against the kitchen counter with his arms folded, 'to know that I've never been interested enough to find out?'

Her eyes, dark with uncertainty, locked with his—so clear and disturbingly penetrating that she wondered how it would be possible for anyone to lie and at the same time look at her like that. But then her father had been a master at it, she remembered bitterly. A prince of deception, so that no one would ever have known...

She brought her thoughts up sharply. Robert Harringdale had lied about everything. His entire life had been a lie. But this was Jarrad, not the capricious character her mother had married, and she could not actually accuse Jarrad Mitchell of ever lying.

He'd never vehemently denied having an affair with

Lauren any more than he'd admitted to it, she reflected. Over a year ago he had responded initially to her accusations only with half-amused remarks to the effect that if she thought he had energy for another woman after all the time he spent in bed with her, she had to think he was some sort of superman. And then, as time progressed, he'd answered with angrier retaliations about it being her problem if she couldn't judge his character enough to trust him.

But had he been lying by omission? Or had Ralph been right today when he had told her that her husband was just unbelievably proud?

'Surprise me,' she whispered, and it was a plea from the heart, without any bitterness or sarcasm. She couldn't have concealed the depth of emotion in her eyes—an emotion she was aching to believe was reflected so starkly in his— if she had tried.

For a moment that silent communication between them was a palpable thing, so strong she could feel it drawing her to him at the same time as he made a move towards her. But then Teeny came hurrying back with some glass dishes, and in the same second the telephone started to ring, so that Kendal found it difficult to pull herself free from her imprisoning emotions and concentrate on something Teeny was saying about whipped cream—particularly as her ears were suddenly straining to catch whatever it was Jarrad was saying as he answered the phone in the hall.

Almost she thought she detected a slight tremor in that deep, authoritative voice, and knew a small thrill in the knowledge that she had affected him like that. That was until he came back and coolly announced, 'That was Lauren. I'm afraid we've had a break-in at the office, and I'm going to have to get down there right away.'

'What, now?' Kendal protested, fighting the suspicion that immediately surfaced like a dark tormentor inside her—the sudden, irrepressible notion that it had been Lauren after all—not her—who had been responsible for that tremor in his voice. 'Can't she handle it?'

''Fraid not.' It seemed his light kiss on her brow was merely perfunctory now as, keys in hand, he was already preparing to leave.

'Speak of the devil?' she couldn't help but throw after him as he was striding out of the door, hating herself for these doubts that continued to attack her like an invisible enemy, and drew a reprehensible look from Teeny Roberts. But what was she supposed to say? Think? When trying as she was to convince herself that his lovely colleague meant nothing to him—had never meant anything to him—as Ralph and Teeny would have her believe, Lauren only had to telephone and he was gone!

'Keep an eye on her, Teeny, will you?' asked Jarrad drily, turning in the doorway. 'And if she misbehaves let me know.'

And you'll do what? she wanted to hurl back, but decided that that would have been extremely childish, especially in view of what Teeny had said to her earlier. She turned broodily away and began fiercely chopping some mushrooms the housekeeper had washed to put into a marinade.

She could feel his eyes boring into her back, willing her to look at him, although sheer bloody-mindedness on her part kept her from doing so, and she caught his rather impatient, indrawn breath before he obviously gave up and strode away.

'And if you say anything about losing him, you should try being on one end of the proverbial triangle, Teeny!' Kendal exhaled, sensing Teeny's disapproval, battling painfully against the old, familiar suspicions.

'A triangle that's going to start clanging pretty loudly in favour of Lauren Westgate if you don't watch it,' was all Teeny responded with, shaming her into silence. But how could the woman even begin to understand the emotions that racked her? she wondered, aggrieved. Teeny adored Jarrad. It was therefore patently clear that she would take his side.

But, no, that wasn't true at all, she admitted fairly after a few moments. There had been times in the past when the woman had taken *her* side over minor issues. No, Teeny just spoke as she found. And in this instance she found Jarrad the injured party and her, Kendal, jealous, petty and unreasonable—had thought her so all along. Hadn't she told her as much this morning? Intimated that she would have known if he'd been having an affair with Lauren? But would she? Kendal agonised. How could anyone ever be certain of anyone else?

'You have to trust him, Kendal.' From behind her Teeny's words came as though in response to her unspoken questions—practical, firm, yet somehow understanding too. And, above the sound of the kettle she was filling to make a cup of tea, 'You have to learn to trust,' she went on to enlarge. 'Because sometimes trust is all there is.'

Kendal was dressed and ready by the time Jarrad arrived back from the office, and, as all he had time for when he dashed in was to rush straight upstairs and shower, they exchanged very few words—only enough for her to establish that several computers and other equipment had been stolen. From the way he had looked at her, though, as he had come into the bedroom, already stripping off his clothes, she knew her appearance had knocked him for six!

She had stopped at a boutique and bought a new dress on the way back from Chrissie's that day, needing a new boost of confidence in the knowledge that she was going to have to face Lauren that evening.

A long, figure-hugging creation in emerald green, it was entirely plain at the front, but with a criss-crossing of shoe-lace straps at the back that offered tantalising glimpses of her creamy flesh, which was a stark contrast to the loose, riotous red of her hair.

'You didn't warn me you were going to look like this.' Jarrad's cool blue eyes were raking appreciatively over her as she glanced up from arranging some fresh flowers in the lounge where he had just joined her. But then he had always said emerald suited her best.

'Did you need any warning?' she remarked, placing the last bright gladiolus in the vase amongst the dark green swords of its neighbours. 'Anyway, you didn't give me the chance.' Because he had dashed off as soon as he had got that call, she remembered, then added as casually as she could, 'I'm surprised you didn't bring Lauren back with you.'

'Are you?'

He was wearing a dark lounge suit with an immaculate white shirt, looking so vitally male with his freshly groomed black hair and olive skin that Kendal had a job taking her eyes off him—battling as she was against the sensations that assailed her from the clean, fresh scent of him as he drew near, from the sheer dynamism his very presence exuded.

'Lauren was tied up elsewhere—that's why she rang me to go and sort things out,' he went on to inform her surprisingly then. 'As a matter of fact, she said she's going to be late.'

'Really?'

Their eyes met and locked.

'Yes,' he said, half exasperated, before his irritation turned swiftly to soft mockery. 'So you've got a couple of hours yet before you need to start worrying about any competition.'

'That's not very funny!'

She would have turned on her heel and swept away from him, out of the lounge, if his arm hadn't shot out and snaked around her middle.

'Would I even joke about it,' he said roughly, pulling her back to face him, 'if it were true?'

Would he?

Her red-tipped hands moved over the sleek fabric covering his shoulders, a little frisson shivering through her as they acknowledged the power-packed strength beneath. How could a woman ever really be sure?

'You've got no competition. You should know that,' he whispered thickly, and even his words were an impossible turn-on against her ripe, red mouth. 'You look more beautiful tonight than I've ever seen you look.'

Oh, Jarrad!

As his mouth opened over hers she leaned into him with all the strength of her yearning, a small protest escaping her as swiftly he withdrew, teasing her, withholding the kiss she craved.

'You wouldn't thank me for that,' he laughed very softly, his gaze skimming over her drooping eyelids to rest on her deprived lips, still parted for his kiss. 'Your lipstick's having the desired effect, but if I kiss it off now it might present the picture to our guests that we can't keep our hands off each other—which I'm sure your pride wouldn't want you to have them think—and I believe the first of them is about to arrive at any second.'

His words hurt, but then, as if on cue, the doorbell pealed, followed by Teeny's hurrying footsteps across the hall.

Despite what he had said, however, Kendal was surprised when Jarrad waited until Paul and Diana Lawrence were coming through the door before he let her go—as though he wanted his colleague and spouse to see that the reconciliation was working. She had to greet them, therefore, with the sensation of that warm hand still burning through her dress, wondering how he could simply switch off his desire for her to play the role of cordial host with such effortless ease, while she had to struggle for her composure and hope her agitation didn't show.

The party was in full swing by the time Lauren turned up. In fact, Kendal didn't even see her arrive.

She had been engrossed in conversation with a small group of people more her own age who, at her suggestion, had taken their drinks outside to make the most of the mild, early autumn night.

Now, though, coming back into the lounge, she saw her.

She was in a black and white silk top which she was wearing with black velvet leggings and black boots. Her hair, Kendal noticed, was longer than it had been in the summer, shaped into a bob, having reverted to its natural colour of ripe wheat, and she looked the most radiant woman in the room.

Standing by the fireplace with a glass of champagne, and the blaze of the gladioli behind her, she was looking up laughingly into Jarrad's eyes. Then someone knocked clumsily against her, almost making her spill her wine, the action forcing her to move forward, bringing her into unbearably intimate contact with Jarrad.

Kendal looked quickly away, telling herself not to be so affected. But her jealousy was rife, and she had to force herself to speak to someone—anyone—to bring her torturing emotions back under control.

'Do you hire out your Mrs Roberts? She's a wonderwoman, isn't she?'

'Yes, she is.' It was an effort even to offer that mechanical response to the wife of one of the under-managers who was enthusing about Teeny's capabilities.

'She's not just a pretty face, either. She's a shrewd woman too,' the woman's husband, who claimed to know their housekeeper, went on to comment.

'Yes, she is,' Kendal murmured again—but thought, Shrewd enough to be right about Jarrad not wanting Lauren? Perhaps she should see them now!

A covert glance over her shoulder, however, revealed Lauren still standing by the fireplace, but, surprisingly, chatting to someone else—although, following Lauren's rather abstracted gaze, Kendal realised it was still fixed on Jarrad.

He was standing on the other side of the room, talking with three of his younger executives, his sophistication and maturity outstripping theirs by light years. There was no doubt from the deferential smiles of two of the men, and the rather over-confident body language of the other, who they wanted to emulate, if not impress.

Though he appeared to be giving them his full attention, however, he seemed preoccupied in some way, as though his mind was on something else entirely. Then he looked up before Kendal could look away, caught her watching him, and the heart-quickening smile he gave her made her bones turn to jelly. How could he look at her like that if he was having an affair with Lauren? If Ralph and Teeny were wrong? He couldn't, surely?

And yet his smile, though touched with a sensual warmth, was abstracted too, she noted, that fine, pensive line between his eyes making him look almost... Almost what? Uneasy? she thought, unable, nevertheless, to drag her gaze away from his raw masculinity, so that when someone spoke just behind her she started.

'You've certainly got a houseful tonight!'

She turned and saw a smiling Paul Lawrence just shouldering his way past with two refilled glasses.

She laughed then, forcing herself to relax. 'Yes, we have!' she agreed in response.

In fact, there were very few people there she didn't recognise from previous company functions.

Briefly her gaze touched on the few faces of the people she hadn't met before, who were mainly executives' wives, then skimmed over their animated heads to the door on the far side of the room, which offered a view straight up the stairs, to the bearded man who was just coming down them.

He came towards the doorway, peered through it as though he was looking for someone—but somewhat furtively, Kendal thought, frowning.

'Excuse me.'

Uneasy, she manoeuvred her way through the happy assembly to the other side of the room, having to politely disentangle herself from one or two guests who clearly wanted to chat. By the time she reached the door and came out into the hall, however, the man was nowhere to be seen.

The front door was open. She closed it, and, about to go upstairs to check on Matthew, had to wait for Teeny who was just hurrying down.

'Matthew,' Kendal breathed, unnecessarily anxious. 'Is he all right?'

'Sleeping like a top,' Teeny reassured her with a smile. 'Be a dear and take these clean teatowels through to the kitchen for me.' She thrust a neatly ironed pile into Kendal's arms. 'And don't worry. I'll check that Matthew's not being disturbed,' she offered, not altogether understanding her concern, Kendal realised as the woman went back upstairs.

In the lounge again, sipping a glass of champagne, Kendal was listening to a large man—with an even larger laugh—extolling the benefits of working for TMS, and in particular her husband's achievements, when Lauren drifted across to them in a waft of exclusive perfume.

'The perfect hostess with the perfect husband and the perfect home!'

Above the buzz of conversation and the light popular music that was playing, Lauren's compliment still somehow managed to pique.

She flashed a smile at Kendal's large companion, the sort of dismissive gesture Kendal guessed she would use to a menial in the office, and Kendal was therefore unsurprised when the man, patting her on the arm, emitted another booming laugh and moved away.

'I'm buying one—a house, that is,' Lauren informed her importantly. 'Something a little less cramped than the flat I've got at present.' She was sipping what looked surprisingly like orange juice—surprisingly, because usually Lauren only stuck to champagne. 'I was wondering if I could enlist your services with the interior. I don't have the time or the inclination to spend on it myself, and I've always admired your flair.'

She cast an appreciative eye over the bold russet of the curtains that picked out the same shade in the cream and russet sofas and the rich tones of the carpet, and the honeyed walnut of the tastefully selected furniture. 'In fact I've rather envied it.'

Well, that was an admission, Kendal thought, coming from Lauren!

'I suppose you realise I've envied a lot of things about you, Kendal.' Her pale hair moved softly as she studied the striking red of Kendal's, the perfection of her make-up— due in part to her artistic abilities—the tantalising, flattering green dress. 'Your taste. Your home. Your husband.' As she said it she sent a sultry glance across the room towards Jarrad, who was laughing at something an elderly woman was saying to him.

Kendal tensed so that it was all she could do to utter, 'Really, Lauren? I'd never have guessed!'

Lauren laughed. 'Well, of course, you've known all along, haven't you? If you hadn't, you'd have been blind or stupid—and you're neither of those things, are you? You wouldn't have kept him this long if you were. Still, I'm pleased to be able to say that that's all in the past—that I really shan't be envying you any more.' Lauren's smile was both patronising and mysterious. 'What about it, then? Can I take it you'll accept the job on my house?'

'I'm afraid I'm not doing that any longer, Lauren,' Kendal told her, puzzled by what the woman had meant about not envying her any more. 'But if you'd like me to recommend someone else, I can,' she added matter-of-factly, thinking of Tony Beeson. 'I shan't be doing any interior work for quite a while. Not until Matthew's much older anyway.'

A curious smile lifted the corners of Lauren's beautiful mouth. 'So he finally put his foot down and you gave in. Well done, Jarrad!' An upward tilt of that confident head exposed the pale column of her throat above the slinky black and white top. 'Although, conversely, one might say, more fool you!'

Kendal edged forward as someone pushed their way past behind her. 'It isn't like that at all!' she responded, nettled. 'And I would have thought, after what happened, Lauren, that you would have been a little more sensitive regarding the subject.'

'Sorry,' was all Lauren said with a casual shrug. But then her smile turned sultry again as she looked up, and Kendal realised why.

Jarrad had joined them, and his dark attraction was totally arresting, the strength of his magnetism almost as terrifying as its ability to excite.

'I didn't realise you were so strong on old-fashioned values, Jarrad.' Lauren purred up at him provocatively. 'The man provides and the woman produces and all that.'

'It wasn't like that at all!' Kendal reiterated, bristling. 'It was very much a joint decision!'

Lauren laughed. 'Oh, he's good at those!' The smile she flashed at Jarrad was almost wicked. 'You should see him in the boardroom! We all think we've come out with the right amount of the share in the decision-making, but, when it boils down to it, there's only one person in control—as I'm sure you know.'

Kendal was beginning to realise that Lauren was turned on by all the power Jarrad represented, even more than by the real man.

'Jarrad's never needed to make any decisions for me, Lauren,' she answered more calmly now, her words falling on uninterested ears as the woman was already moving away.

'Perhaps I should have.'

The deep, smooth tones brought Kendal's head up challengingly in rebellion. He was laughing down at her, his cool blue eyes totally amused.

'What's the matter, Kendal? Don't you like people believing you're a slave to my every whim?' he murmured, his hand moving with electrifying sensuality over the alluring straps criss-crossing her spine.

She sucked in her breath, her back stiffening at his casual yet overtly proprietorial caress, and she opened her mouth to make some swift rejoinder, saw that he was only teasing her with those chauvinistic comments, and thought better of it.

But it wasn't only that. There seemed to be a different sort of intercommunication between Jarrad and Lauren tonight, and it wasn't helped by the fact that Kendal had never seen the other woman look lovelier. During the past hour or so, while Jarrad's smile had lost its relaxed ease, Lauren had appeared to glow, and looked strangely smug. Her relationship with her senior colleague, though always openly provocative, now hinted at some sort of devil-may-care attitude that Kendal couldn't quite put her finger on.

Nevertheless, it was unsettling, to say the least, and with a cool glance at Jarrad she pulled away from that disturbing hand and did her best for the rest of the evening to be an entertaining hostess for the sake of his other colleagues—refilling glasses, taking round the finger buffet that she and Teeny had prepared earlier, keeping a smile pasted on her face as she tried to show an interest in everything being said to her.

In spite of that, though, all she seemed to be aware of above the music and the voices of the other guests was Lauren's bright laughter, Lauren's witty comments, Lauren's intelligent conversation. Kendal was aware, too, of the way she smiled at Jarrad every time he happened to move into her sphere—as though the two of them were nursing some very private secret.

Unable to take it any longer, Kendal knew she had to get away for a few minutes by herself.

But, no, not completely by herself, she thought as she eventually made her way, unimpeded, to the stairs, feeling a sudden, overwhelming need to be with Matthew.

His door, she was pleased to see, was still pulled to,

shutting out a lot of the party noise. The small bedside lamp she had left burning earlier cast a subtle glow over one corner of the room and the motley crew of teddies that were looking out from the depths of his blue baby chair towards the empty cot.

The empty cot!

A ridiculous fear gripped her stomach as she moved towards it, sending an anxious glance around the room.

His covers were barely disturbed, and, puzzled, she reached down into the cot and ripped them back, as though to convince herself that he wasn't actually there. There was only his blue teddy, discarded beside the pillow!

Where was he?

Perhaps Teeny had taken him to the bathroom, she reasoned, darting down to the main suite, although she knew, even before she reached it and found it deserted, that that wasn't very likely.

Jarrad must have moved him to another room because of the noise downstairs, she decided. She was only overreacting because of what had happened before.

It was with a sense of increasing urgency, however, that she flew along the landing, darting in and out of every room.

Deserted!

Panic seized her, the frightening memory of that awful Friday back in June and the torturous week that had followed filling her with intensifying dread.

Don't panic. He'll be with Teeny, she rationalised, although her feet barely touched the stairs as she descended into a well of music and laughter and conversation, her mind filled only with the picture of that stranger—the bearded man she had seen earlier—coming down the stairs!

What if someone—what if *he*—had taken him?

'Hey, Kendal! Hang on a minute! What's the rush?' Someone hailed her from amidst the party that had spilled out into the hall. 'Have you got time to—?'

Time to what? She didn't linger to find out, not caring

if she did appear rude. She had to find Matthew—and quickly!

Almost colliding with Teeny, who was coming out of the kitchen, she stopped only to gasp, 'Have you seen Matthew?'

The plate of prawn vol-au-vents Teeny was holding was deliciously enhanced by sprigs of dark green parsley, but Kendal didn't spare it a second glance.

'Isn't he in bed?'

That was all Kendal needed to make her turn, without even answering, and force her way back through the hall.

No, he isn't! Her mind clamoured with near paralysing fear, because she knew Jarrad didn't have him. She had seen him outside, talking to Paul and another man on the patio, before going upstairs, and Matthew hadn't been with him then!

Someone grasped her arm as she turned into the lounge. 'I do like your home!' she had to endure the older woman saying, but somehow she managed to shrug her off, not caring how it looked.

Shaking, her face pale with consternation, she pushed her way with mounting anxiety and frustration through the impeding barrage of bodies, seeing them only as clowns in some hideous circus act, the music and laughter and loud conversation a parody of real life, torturing her, mocking her fear.

'Jarrad!' He was still there, in the quiet space between the patio and the cedar tree and the animated group of young people she had been speaking to earlier who were chatting over by the old sundial. 'Jarrad! It's Matthew! I can't find him anywhere! I've—'

She broke off abruptly, her gaze skittering to the shadows of the cedar as she heard a sound, saw someone emerge from behind its massive trunk.

Lauren was holding Matthew, bending her head to clear a low-growing branch as she came towards Kendal. She was bouncing the fretful little toddler on her arm.

'I hope you don't mind.' Those confident tones of Lauren's told her she didn't care whether Kendal minded or not. 'You see, I'm just getting in some practice.'

Through the weakening relief that threatened to buckle her knees at finding Matthew safe, Kendal struggled to comprehend what the woman was saying.

Perplexity lined her face, illuminated by the lamps that were cleverly concealed within the cedar's spreading branches. 'Practice?' she queried as a burst of laughter drifted across the garden and music throbbed from inside the house. She looked at Lauren askance.

'Mmm,' Lauren crooned and glanced at something over Kendal's shoulder. The dreamy look that had been there for most of the evening came into her eyes again. 'Yes, I'm pregnant. Didn't Jarrad tell you?' Dreamy—because it was Jarrad she was looking at.

'Lauren!'

In a stunned daze, Kendal heard his whispered remonstration, and whether the other men had heard—or whether they had gone back inside—she didn't know. She only knew that her relief at finding Matthew, coupled with what could only be taken as Jarrad's admission of the ultimate infidelity, had proved too much.

Her head started to spin, and she swayed, aware of nothing then but a burst of laughter from inside the house, Jarrad's soft curse and the hard ground coming up to meet her.

CHAPTER TEN

WHEN Kendal opened her eyes she was lying on the cool leather of the couch in Jarrad's study, and she guessed that he had carried her in there by way of the kitchen to avoid everyone in the lounge. She could still hear the party going on along the hall, but more subdued now, as though a lot of their guests had already left.

'Where's Matthew?' Remembering brought fear surging back, and had her sitting up with her urgent need to know—but a bit too quickly, as it happened, so that a rush of dizziness overtook her, and, with her hand against her forehead, she flopped back down with a groan.

'He's all right.' Jarrad's reply was swift and reasssuring. He was the only one in the room, the subdued light of the desk lamp showing a natural concern in his striking features as he crouched there beside her. 'Teeny has him. More to the point...' She flinched from the hand that touched her cheek, not certain why. Only knowing that she had to. 'How do you feel? You fainted, if you hadn't realised, out there in the garden.'

Of course. Lauren's announcement.

A wave of desolation coursed over her, washing the last of her giddiness away.

'I'm all right,' she murmured feebly, only she wasn't. The world had just ended, out there under the cedar tree, and yet by some cruel miracle she had survived the terrible holocaust, waking up to find that there was nothing but emptiness left.

'I'm not so sure.'

What does it matter to you? she thought torturedly, closing her eyes, for a moment too paralysed by the agony of her emotions to move.

A chorus of groans drifted out from the lounge with the first strains of a resonant classical piece someone had substituted for the beaty, modern tempo that had just finished playing.

Right on cue! Kendal thought bitterly, wondering how, of all the tunes in the world, fate could have ordained that someone choose to play her wedding music now.

'Answer me something truthfully, Kendal.' Some unfathomable emotion darkened the blue eyes level with hers. 'You aren't pregnant too, are you?'

Oh, no! I haven't been that much of a fool! she thought, battling against an unbearable anguish, because after their bitter-sweet lovemaking weeks ago—when she had realised the power he still had over her—she had gone straight to the doctor's and made sure of taking precautions.

Shaking her head, however, it was all she could do to utter, 'Don't worry, Jarrad. You won't have two of us slapping an unexpected paternity suit on you, if that's what you're worried about.' And in a tight, choked voice she went on, 'I presume she's keeping it. Well, congratulations!'

He drew in a short, sharp breath. 'Yes, that's what it sounded like, didn't it?' he rasped.

'What? That she's keeping it? Or that it's yours?' she almost sobbed, emotion ravaging her beneath the tantalising green dress. The dress, she realised with bitter self-mockery, that she had bought to please him. Oh, what a fool! 'Why don't you just deny that she's even pregnant?' she breathed, her green eyes dark with pain.

'I'm afraid I can't deny that,' he stated almost wryly. And she thought, Oh, God! I don't know how much more of this I can take!

'She sprung it on me tonight.' Jarrad's voice was clipped. 'Not long after she arrived.'

So she hadn't imagined that anxiety about him, Kendal realised. That smugness of Lauren's.

'It must have been quite a blow,' she choked, 'having your wife find out like that before you could tell her!'

He got up then, moving across to throw the door closed—or almost closed. She could still hear the muffled voices of people chatting in the hall. And that music...

She sucked in her breath, feeling every note like a knife penetrating, deepening her already gaping wounds.

'Yes, she certainly let you know it without any pretensions to subtlety, didn't she?' he breathed as he came back to her. 'But damn her for making it sound like it was mine—and damn you for believing it!' There was a savage intensity in those features looming above hers that she couldn't understand any more than she could quite comprehend what he was saying.

'Lauren's got a boyfriend,' he went on brusquely, 'and she might even talk herself into marrying him if she can accept a man as her equal long enough to realise he's not some superior being she has to continually prove herself to! She has rather gone against the terms of her contract, though, and decided to leave during the next two months, which does pose a few problems for the company in replacing her. But Gareth is moving away, and therefore she wants to go with him.

'I thought you might have seen him earlier, when he dropped her off—or perhaps you were outside. He couldn't stay as he was driving up to Manchester this evening, but Lauren wanted him to meet me, and so he popped in for a few minutes. A tall chap with a beard...'

So that's who it was! 'The man I saw coming downstairs...'

'What?' She saw Jarrad frown. 'Possibly,' he said, and until then she hadn't realised she had spoken aloud. 'He did ask to use the bathroom before he left.'

Kendal stared at him incredulously. 'Then...it isn't yours...?'

'I've told you,' he said firmly, dropping to his haunches again. 'Or no—maybe I haven't.' There was exasperation and something remarkably like self-rebuke behind the grimace he pulled. 'I've just been hoping you'd have the sense to realise that Lauren means nothing to me beyond a very efficient—and sometimes infuriating—colleague.'

She raised herself up now, trying to digest what he was saying, her gaze sweeping over those elegantly clad shoulders down to where the dark fabric pulled tautly over the hard, bunched muscles of his thighs.

'But you...' She took a deep breath and tried again. 'Ralph saw you,' she reminded him with lines furrowing her brow. 'He told me—reluctantly it's true—but he told me he saw you. You and Lauren in your office that day—wrapped in an intimate clinch!'

'Not exactly,' he disputed, with something curling his mouth at the corners, and now he closed the gap between them and came and sat down on the couch beside her. 'I'd just found out that my sister-in-law's husband—a man I respected and trusted—had been dipping into company funds, and I wasn't sure how I was going to handle it. I was devastated, and Lauren...I suppose she was consoling me.

'And not in the way you think!' he tagged on admonishingly, before Kendal could come out with one of her usual sceptical comments. 'She had her hands on my shoulders—that was all. And that was all that Ralph saw and interpreted as a full-blown love affair. And you were more than ready to believe it. It was only coincidence—an unfortunate one, I know—that he was asked to leave only a matter of days after that.

'Oh, Lauren wanted to make more of our relationship when she knew we'd split up!' he went on to inform her. 'But you should know, darling, that she really isn't my type. I wanted to explain to you—weeks ago—when we were in the Lake District, the day we got Matthew back. Try to convince you—but you seemed so determined to hold out against me—so cold. I thought that perhaps all there was left between us—where you were concerned anyway—was this amazing physical thing we have together.

'But when I made love to you you cried, and I couldn't bear to think that you didn't really want to be there with me, even though I knew that, physically, you couldn't help yourself. That's why I haven't—why I couldn't go through with making love to you the other night. Not because I wanted to hurt or humiliate you in any way, but because I just didn't want you to despise me for making you want me—any more than you already did.'

She couldn't believe that he was saying this. That he was humbling himself with such an outpouring of emotion for her.

'But when we were living together—I mean before—you never did anything to try and prove that there *wasn't* anything going on between you and Lauren,' she murmured in tortured accusation.

'Because I couldn't,' he said wryly. 'Not in any tangible way—any way that I knew I could make you believe. You were suspicious of everything I did. That day you found those receipts and told me that they just confirmed I was having an affair with her, I knew I'd only compounded your suspicions by not telling you we were working away together. But I knew beforehand how you'd react if I did.

'And, yes, you were right when you accused me of keeping back those receipts because I didn't want them winding up on Ralph's desk—but only because I didn't want him to realise we were investigating him, that we were staying up in town sorting things out with our auditors because we already suspected there was something underhand going on.

'Oh, I knew you had a pretty low opinion of my sex in general—which was why it was so hard to get you to go out with me in the first place, why I had to go to such devious lengths to get you into my life at all. But when you told me about your father—what happened to…your mother—I knew that any man would have a job convincing you he could be trusted after a pretty low legacy like that.'

'But you didn't even try to convince me,' she said, puzzled. 'Not then, or even when I came back…'

He stretched his arm along the back of the couch behind her, his breath leaving his lungs with a certain element of self-reproach. 'Because, I think, I just wanted you simply to trust me—trust and accept that what we had between us was enough—all by yourself. I know it's crazy, but I've had my pride too, and when a man is accused of wanting someone else by the one person he'd move heaven and earth for… Well…'

She felt that broad shoulder move beside her, and she thought, Isn't that what Ralph said? That he's proud?

'We just kept slipping further and further apart, and all you seemed to want was your job. I was happy for you to have your career, but you seemed to use it just to push me further and further away from you.'

Had she?

'I couldn't even talk to you,' he said surprisingly then. 'And by the time that thing happened with Ralph…' There was a sudden tautness to his features. Or was it just the shadows caused by the splintered light of the lamp? 'Even if I'd told you the real reason I'd been forced to let him go, I doubt if you would have accepted it as simply as that. Suspicion had built such an impenetrable barrier between us, and it seemed I couldn't do anything else except sit and watch my marriage collapse—although I really never thought you'd leave.

'Chrissie losing her baby was the final straw. When you blamed me for it and left, you plunged me into hell. That was bad enough—but then, when you slipped out of my life for those six months and I couldn't find you, I thought 'd go insane! I think I had poor Teeny on the brink of handing in her notice, as well as several colleagues in the office.

'But then you turned up that day, saying you were going abroad, and I knew I had to get us back together somehow or I'd lose you for good. Then events took a turn that neither of us could have anticipated, and it seemed I had you at the expense of Matthew and I didn't care what you thought about me any more.'

His voice was husky with emotion. Even so she couldn't help saying woundedly, 'Is that why you were so threatening and objectionable towards me?'

'Was I?' The hand behind her lifted to catch a tendril of red hair, twisting it around a finger, his touch as gentle as his voice had been soft. 'I suppose I thought you deserved it,' he said, his sigh one of positive self-censure. 'You were still determined to think the worst about me—no matter what I did. But you still wanted to make love with me, and that was all I had to hang on to. Because if I hadn't been so sure all along that somewhere inside—somewhere amongst all the suspicion and doubt and agony we've been through in losing each other and then Matthew—you still loved me...'

The crack in his voice brought her head up. How could she deny it when every last part of her wanted to trust him, was throbbing with the need to have him love her again, just as the undulating music seemed to be throbbing through the very walls of the house. Their music, she thought, and was so moved that she had to turn aside, keep her eyes trained on the dark leather of the couch as she uttered in a choked, but nevertheless rebellious little voice, 'What makes you so sure about that?'

'Because feelings of uncertainty and suspicion and jealousy only arise from really caring for someone,' she heard him saying then. 'And you've never stopped being uncertain or suspicious since the day you first discovered Lauren was my colleague. Because you still respond to me whenever I touch you.' His voice was a rough whisper. 'Kiss you…'

Gently then he reached round and caught her chin so that, exposed, she had no choice but to look at him, and there was such raw agony in his face it made her gasp. 'And because…' With a light brush of his thumb he wiped away the silent tear that ran betrayingly down her cheek. 'Beçause Pachelbel still makes you cry.'

'Oh, Jarrad!'

On a surge of emotion she turned into the arms that were reaching for her, catching her roughly to him—and she responded eagerly, clasping him to her with every ounce of the love that filled her being.

'I was only going abroad because I wanted to try and forget you—because I thought that the more distance I could put between us the freer I'd feel from those feelings, although I knew, deep down, I never would be free. To get myself involved in a really demanding job seemed to be the only way to get my mind off you.

'Before…I only worked because I felt so insignificant, and I was worried that you'd come to see me like that too. Teeny saw to all your needs around the house, and Lauren…Lauren was so clever and successful she always made me feel so inadequate. I wanted to be everything to you,' she sobbed. 'That's why I worked so hard. I suppose I was hiding behind it too—behind my career,' she admitted sniffily then. 'But I wanted to be a wife and mother and successful in a career as well so that I could make you proud of me. I never realised how much I was neglecting the people I care about just by trying so hard to earn your love.'

Because she had, hadn't she? Sometimes he had been in pain, and she hadn't even noticed. Hadn't even been aware of the problems that were building, ticking away like a time-bomb, in her own sister. 'Forgive me.'

'Why?' There was a chuckle in the words he spoke into her silky perfumed hair. 'For being you? You never needed to earn my love. You've always had it,' he said in a hoarse, controlled voice. 'And you need never, never try and prove yourself to me. You're everything I want—everything I've ever wanted. Everything I need. You must know that.'

'Tell me again,' she murmured against the lips that were hovering above hers, and he did, blotting out any last shred of uncertainty in the hard excitement of his kiss.

When eventually he broke apart from her it was only to say, 'And if you're worried about Teeny usurping your position as mistress of this house—don't be. She's already said things are getting a bit too much for her, and she wants to take a far less demanding role in the future.'

Surprise showed in Kendal's eyes. But Teeny wasn't only thinking of herself, she realised with a soft, fond smile for Jarrad's devoted and remarkably caring housekeeper. She wanted to give them space.

'Promise me you'll never let anything come between us again.' He breathed the husky command against her cheek. 'Not your career, or any crazy doubts or suspicions...'

With her eyes closed, her hair falling in a cascade of fire across his arm, she murmured her assent.

'And promise me something else.'

Her eyelashes fluttered open. She didn't want to talk.

'What?' she murmured, her lips against the rough velvet of his throat.

'That I'll always have your trust.'

There was such stark emotion in his face that she had to reach up and draw her fingers gently down that hard, beloved cheek.

He wasn't like her father, and she had been so grossly wrong in ever assuming that he was. He had pride, it was true, but he also had ethics and principles and integrity—qualities that Robert Harringdale had never had.

What was it Teeny had said? That you had to learn to

trust, because sometimes trust was all there was? Well, trusting too much might have destroyed her mother, but she was beginning to realise now that trusting too little destroyed equally as much—marriages. Respect. People's love for each other. Just as she had nearly destroyed her own marriage with her own inability to trust.

Lauren had never been a threat, not where Jarrad was concerned; surprisingly Kendal realised she was ready to accept that now. Because of her parents' marriage she had been imbued with so many insecurities, and Lauren had known and played upon those insecurities, and, like a fool, Kendal had let her!

'Always,' she breathed in answer to his question, and, to make sure of doubly convincing him, murmured, 'For ever,' drawing his head down to seal her promise with a kiss.

Those familiar sensations started building inside her, but so much more intense now, with the certainty of his love, and from the groan that came from his throat she knew he was experiencing the same intensity of desire. His arms caught her to him with crushing possession, and he was breathing as irregularly as she was when he broke the kiss.

'How soon do you think we could get rid of this lot?' He was more than a little serious as he jerked his head towards the door.

Kendal laughed, a delightful little frisson running through her.

'We've got all our lives for that!' she breathed, wishing as much as he was for the time when they could be alone.

Jarrad gave a wry grimace. 'Not for what I've got in mind.'

'Jarrad Mitchell!' Another little thrill ran through her. 'What can you be contemplating?'

'You'd be surprised,' he grinned.

Suddenly, though, those strong features took on a more serious cast and he said, 'When you fainted just now and

I thought you were pregnant again I couldn't think of any-thing I wanted more. And it wasn't only all the talk of Lauren being pregnant. It's something that's been on my mind for weeks. I seriously think Matthew needs a play-mate, a little brother or sister, and a two-and-a-half-year or so gap would be just about right. Apart from which, I couldn't think of a better way to celebrate our getting back together. It could be my reconciliation gift to you...'

With eyes that were moist with emotion, Kendal couldn't contain a crooked little smile.

'You mean nappies and feeding bottles and sleepless nights!' she reminded him, but she was only joking. 'I like presents,' she murmured provocatively against his lips then, and, with her hand sliding down his chest to the dark band encircling his hard, firm waist, she looked up at him with a tantalising smile and said, 'When can I take off the wrap-ping?'

His groan was a mixture of need and frustration. 'We've got to dispense with a few superfluous commodities first.' She didn't even need to see the grimace he sent towards the door.

'What do you suppose would happen,' she said, laugh-ing, 'if I went out there and shouted "fire"?'

The sound of Matthew's fretful little voice outside the door, followed by a knock, made them both look up before Teeny came in, carrying her little charge. She looked re-lieved that Kendal was all right, and was quick to grasp the situation with a satisfied smile.

'I'm sorry, Kendal—sir—but he wouldn't let me put him to bed. He's never going to settle unless he's with you.'

Bearing out Teeny's remark, he stopped fretting the in-stant she put him down, and went toddling up to Jarrad's outstretched arms.

'Well, what's your opinion, Matthew?'

Lovingly, Kendal watched him swing the little boy up onto his lap—a precious little gift created out of their love for each other. Just as the next one would be, she mused blissfully, meeting the emotion in Jarrad's eyes over Matthew's tiny head and wishing—just as she knew he was—that everyone else would be as diplomatic as Teeny and just simply disappear.

'What do you suppose would happen,' he said, 'if Mummy shouted "fire"?'

And Matthew, laughing up at them, clapped his little hands together, drawing a burst of laughter from them both as he shouted with precision-timed innocence, 'All goh!'

MILLS & BOON®

Next Month's Romances

♡

Each month you can choose from a wide variety of romance novels from Mills & Boon. Below are the new titles to look out for next month from the Presents™ and Enchanted™ series.

Presents™

Dishonourable Intent	Anne Mather
The Reluctant Fiancée	Jacqueline Baird
Marriage on the Rebound	Michelle Reid
The Divorcee Said Yes!	Sandra Marton
Wildcat Wife	Lindsay Armstrong
The Secret Mother	Lee Wilikinson
That Kind of Man	Sharon Kendrick
Wild and Willing!	Kim Lawrence

Enchanted™

The Fortunes of Francesca	Betty Neels
Shotgun Marriage	Day Leclaire
Holding on to Alex	Margaret Way
Bride By Day	Rebecca Winters
Wife for Real	Jennifer Taylor
Marriage Bait	Eva Rutland
Wild Horses!	Ruth Jean Dale
Help Wanted: Daddy	Carolyn Greene

Available from WH Smith, John Menzies, Volume One, Forbuoys, Martins, Tesco, Asda, and other paperback stockists.

LYNN
ERICKSON

Night Whispers

Someone is watching her every move...

Anna Dunning is living a nightmare. A stalker
is on the prowl and her only hope is a tough
ex-cop—but can she trust him?

*"...shadowy and suspenseful, leaving the reader with
a creepy, unsettled feeling of
expectation."*—Publishers Weekly

1-55166-178-0
AVAILABLE FROM DECEMBER 1997

Barbara

DELINSKY

THE DREAM

She'd do anything to save her family home.

Jessica Crosslyn was prepared for the challenge of saving
her family's home—but she wasn't prepared to share the
project with Carter Malloy, a man she loathed. They
could work together to restore the house, but mending
past mistakes proved to be more difficult.

*"When you care to read the very best, the name of
Barbara Delinsky should come immediately to
mind."*—Rave Reviews

WINTER WARMERS

How would you like to win a year's supply of Mills & Boon® books? Well you can and they're FREE! Simply complete the competition below and send it to us by 30th June 1998. The first five correct entries picked after the closing date will each win a year's subscription to the Mills & Boon series of their choice. What could be easier?

THERMAL SOCKS	RAINCOAT	RADIATOR
TIGHTS	WOOLY HAT	CARDIGAN
BLANKET	SCARF	LOG FIRE
WELLINGTONS	GLOVES	JUMPER

T	H	E	R	M	A	L	S	O	C	K	S
I	Q	S	R	E	P	M	U	J	I	N	O
G	A	S	T	I	S	N	O	I	O	E	E
H	T	G	R	A	D	I	A	T	O	R	L
T	A	C	A	R	D	I	G	A	N	A	T
S	H	F	G	O	L	N	Q	S	W	I	E
J	Y	H	J	K	I	Y	R	C	A	N	K
H	L	F	N	L	W	E	T	A	N	C	N
B	O	V	L	O	G	F	I	R	E	O	A
D	O	E	A	D	F	G	J	F	K	A	L
C	W	A	E	G	L	O	V	E	S	T	B

C7L

Please turn over for details of how to enter ⇨

HOW TO ENTER

There is a list of twelve items overleaf all of which are used to keep you warm and dry when it's cold and wet. Each of these items, is hidden somewhere in the grid for you to find. They may appear forwards, backwards or diagonally. As you find each one, draw a line through it. When you have found all twelve, don't forget to fill in the coupon below, pop this page into an envelope and post it today—you don't even need a stamp! Hurry competition ends 30th June 1998.

Mills & Boon Winter Warmers Competition FREEPOST CN81, Croydon, Surrey, CR9 3WZ

EIRE readers send competition to PO Box 4546, Dublin 24.

Please tick the series you would like to receive if you are one of the lucky winners

Presents™ ❏ Enchanted™ ❏ Medical Romance™ ❏
Historical Romance™ ❏ Temptation® ❏

Are you a Reader Service™ Subscriber?　　Yes ❏　No ❏

Mrs/Ms/Miss/Mr........................Initials ....
(BLOCK CAPITALS PLEASE)

Surname ....

Address ....

....

.....................................Postcode ....

(I am over 18 years of age)　　　　　　　　　　　　C7L

One application per household. Competition open to residents of the UK and Ireland only. You may be mailed with offers from other reputable companies as a result of this application. If you would prefer not to receive such offers, please tick box. ❏

Mills & Boon® is a registered trademark of Harlequin Mills & Boon Limited.